GC120
Worksheets

Created by the faculty in Graphic Communications
Revised by Ted Branoff and Kathleen Mapson

North Carolina State University
College of Education
Department of Science, Technology, Engineering, and
Mathematics Education

Revised Fall 2014

Study the examples printed in dark color with respect to proportion, order of strokes, and the position of each stroke. Construct freehand a large figure in the box provided using the proper strokes and maintaining the correct proportion. Construct additional copies of each figure in the space provided.

Study the examples printed in dark color with respect to proportion, order of strokes, and the position of each stroke. Construct freehand a large figure in the box provided using the proper strokes and maintaining the correct proportion. Construct additional copies of each figure in the space provided.

DRAWN BY:		TITLE:		LET20
COURSE:	SECTION:	SCALE:	DATE:	REV 2008

Study the examples printed in dark color with respect to proportion, order of strokes, and the position of each stroke. Construct freehand a large figure in the box provided using the proper strokes and maintaining the correct proportion. Construct additional copies of each figure in the space provided.

DRAWN BY:

COURSE:　　　　SECTION:　　SCALE:　　　　DATE:

TITLE:

LET 30

REV 2008

GRAPHIC COMMUNICATIONS

1. DIMENSIONS PLACED HORIZONTALLY ON THE DRAWING SHOULD BE READ FROM THE BOTTOM OF THE DRAWING.

2. DIMENSIONS PLACED VERTICALLY ON THE DRAWING SHOULD BE READ FROM THE RIGHT SIDE OF THE DRAWING.

3. DIMENSIONS ARE USUALLY PLACED BETWEEN THE VIEWS OF THE DRAWING.

4. DIMENSION LINES SHOULD NOT CROSS ANY OTHER LINE ON THE DRAWING.

5. OVERALL DIMENSIONS SHOULD ALWAYS BE SPECIFIED ON THE DRAWING.

6. NOTES SHOULD ALWAYS BE PLACED HORIZONTALLY ON THE DRAWING.

7. DIMENSIONS SHOULD NOT BE REPEATED ON THE DRAWING.

8. THE SCALE OF THE DRAWING SHOULD ALWAYS BE SPECIFIED.

9. GUIDE LINES SHOULD BE DRAWN FOR LETTERING IN NOTES, TITLES, ETC.

10. DIMENSIONS MUST BE EASILY READ FROM A DISTANCE OF 3 FEET.

GRAPHIC COMMUNICATIONS

DRAWN BY:

TITLE:

LET 060

COURSE:

SECTION:

SCALE:

DATE:

REV 2013

In the space below-extend and duplicate the Alphabet of lines. Label each line with its name using 3mm lettering spaced below the line. Use the given guide lines. Appropriate line thickness should be maintained for each line type.

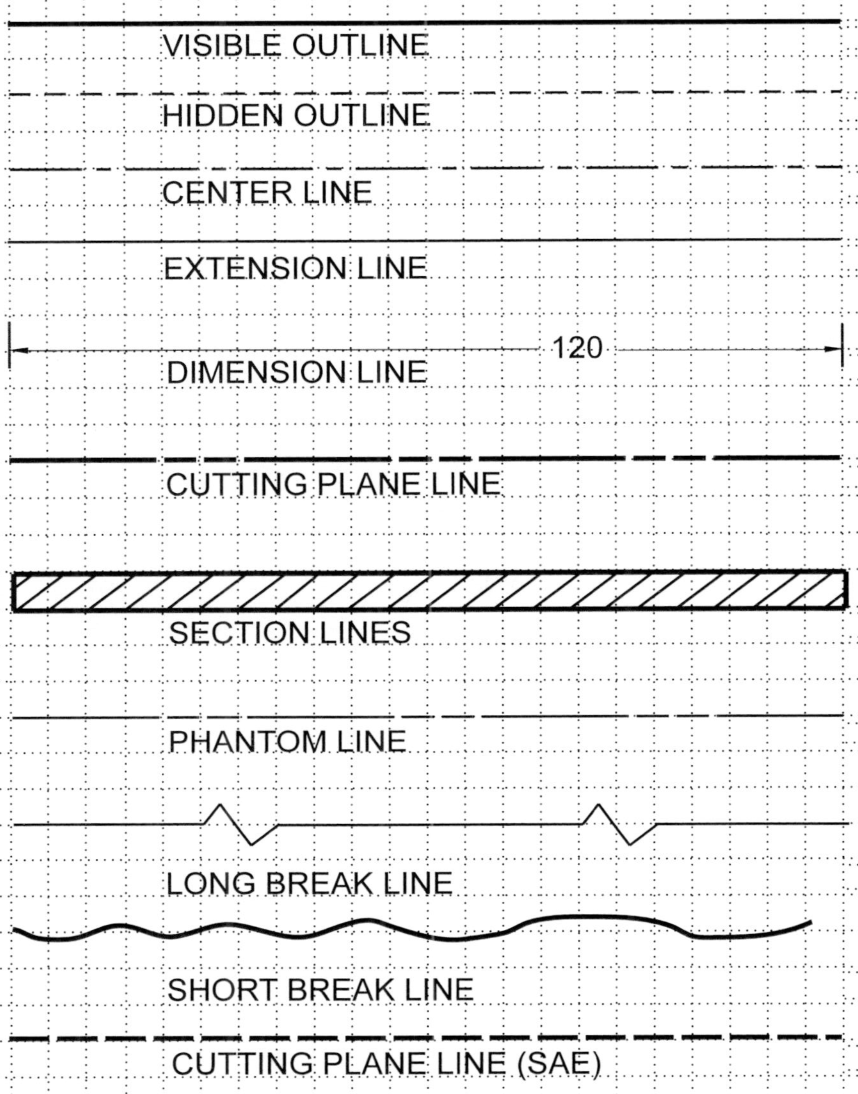

VISIBLE OUTLINE

HIDDEN OUTLINE

CENTER LINE

EXTENSION LINE

DIMENSION LINE

120

CUTTING PLANE LINE

SECTION LINES

PHANTOM LINE

LONG BREAK LINE

SHORT BREAK LINE

CUTTING PLANE LINE (SAE)

DRAWN BY:

COURSE:

TITLE:

SECTION:

SCALE:

DATE:

GRAPHIC COMMUNICATIONS

INS 040

REV 2013

Sketch an equilateral triangle
using A-B as the base.

Sketch a square
using E-F as the base.

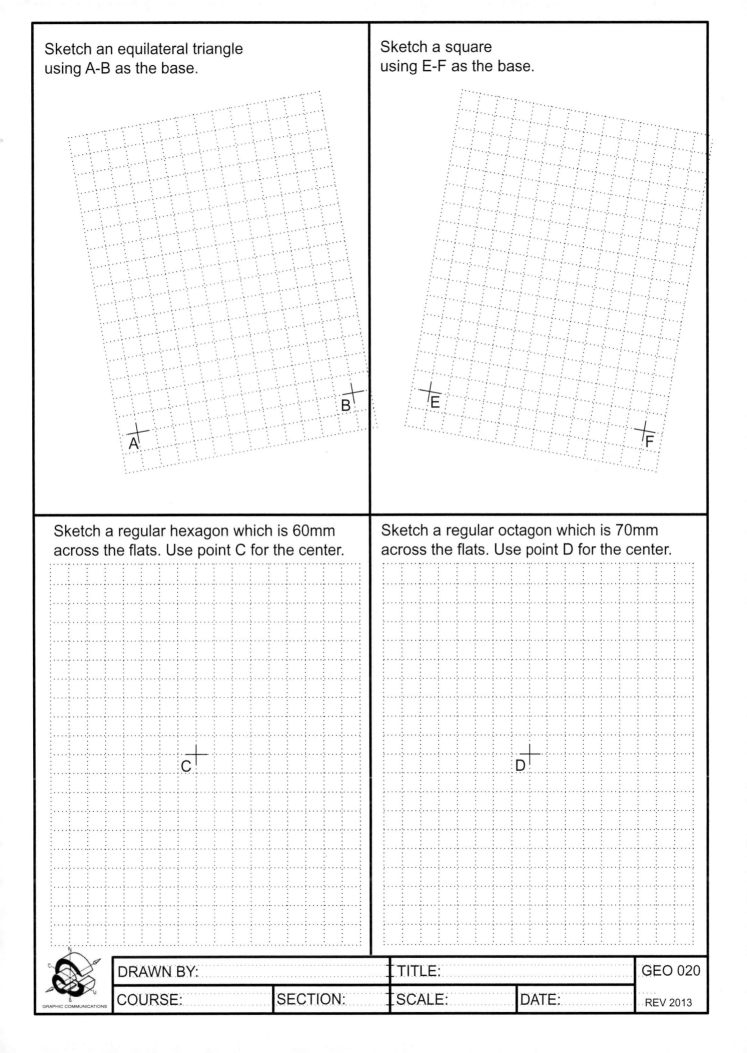

A

B

E

F

Sketch a regular hexagon which is 60mm
across the flats. Use point C for the center.

Sketch a regular octagon which is 70mm
across the flats. Use point D for the center.

C

D

GRAPHIC COMMUNICATIONS

DRAWN BY:		TITLE:		GEO 020
COURSE:	SECTION:	SCALE:	DATE:	REV 2013

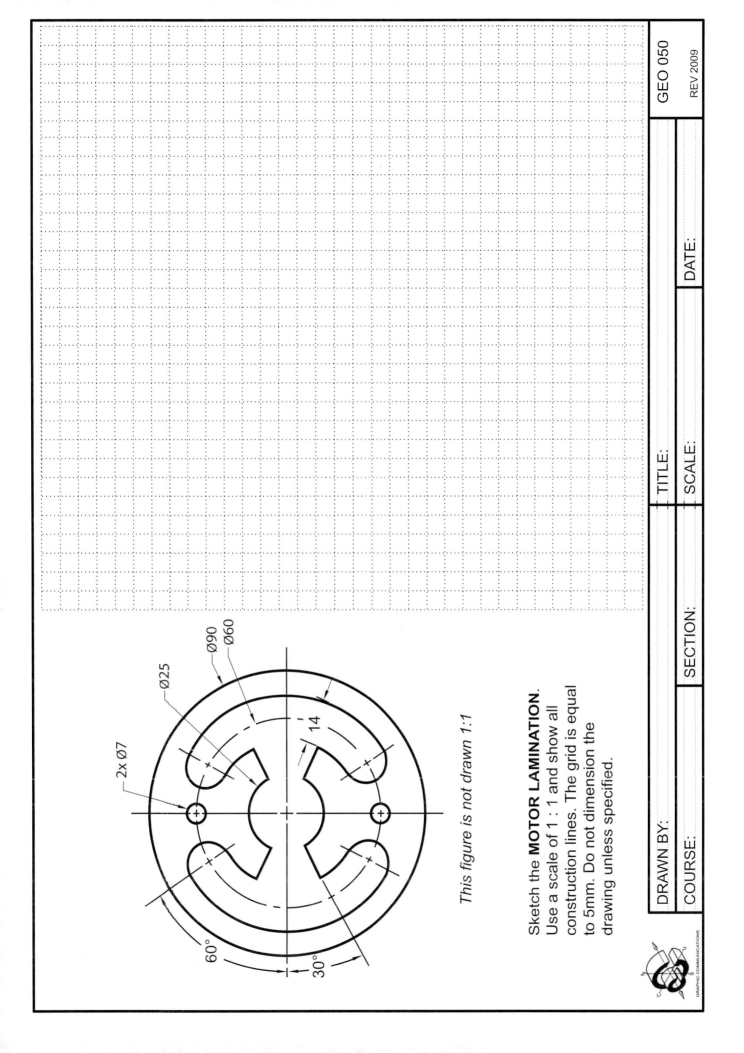

Ø90
Ø60
Ø25
2x Ø7
14
60°
30°

This figure is not drawn 1:1

Sketch the **MOTOR LAMINATION**.
Use a scale of 1 : 1 and show all
construction lines. The grid is equal
to 5mm. Do not dimension the
drawing unless specified.

GRAPHIC COMMUNICATIONS

DRAWN BY:

COURSE:

SECTION:

TITLE:

SCALE:

DATE:

GEO 050

REV 2009

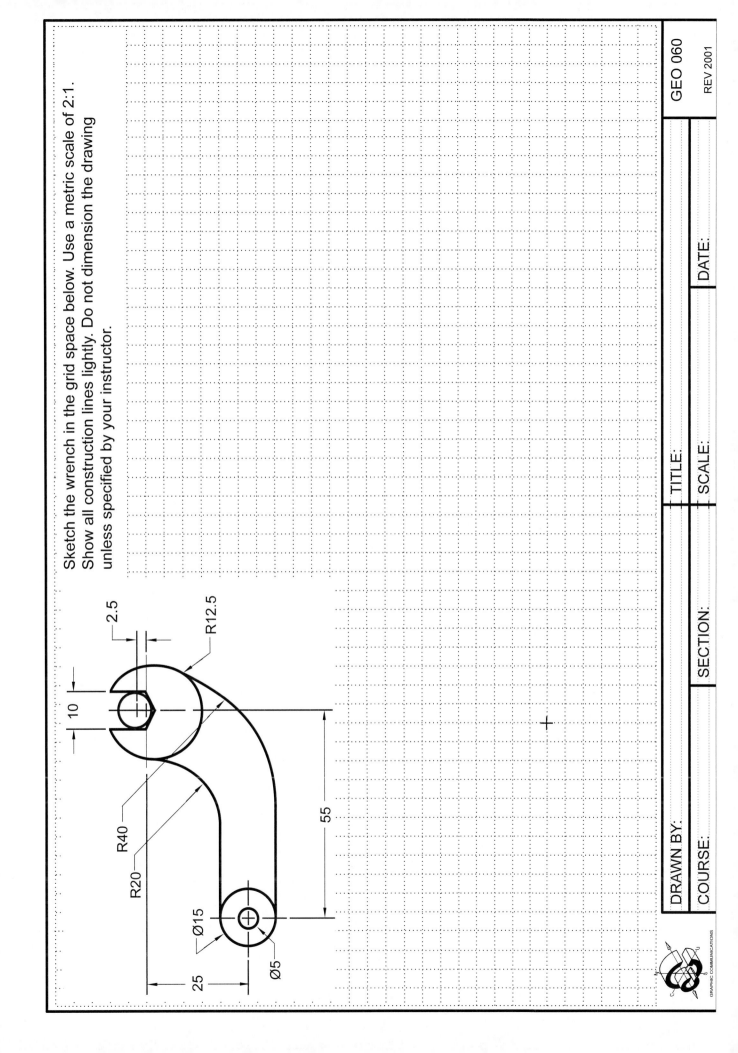

Sketch the wrench in the grid space below. Use a metric scale of 2:1. Show all construction lines lightly. Do not dimension the drawing unless specified by your instructor.

2.5

R12.5

10

R40

R20

55

Ø15

Ø5

25

GEO 060

REV 2001

TITLE:

DATE:

SCALE:

DRAWN BY:

SECTION:

COURSE:

GRAPHIC COMMUNICATIONS

Label the geometric relationships found in the drawing with the appropriate letter to the RIGHT of the relationship.

	GEOMETRIC RELATIONSHIPS
A	Parallel
B	Perpendicular
C	Midpoint
D	Coincident
E	Horizontal
F	Vertical
G	Colinear
H	Equal
I	Tangent
J	Concentric
K	Symmetric
L	At The Origin

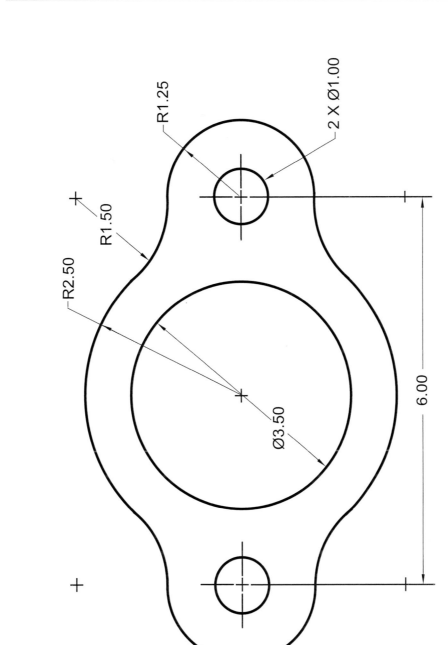

R1.25

R1.50

R2.50

2 X Ø1.00

Ø3.50

6.00

DRAWN BY:		TITLE:	GEO 100
COURSE:	SECTION:	SCALE:	DATE:

REV 2004

Label the geometric relationships found in the drawing with the appropriate letter to the RIGHT of the relationship.

GEOMETRIC RELATIONSHIPS	
A	Parallel
B	Perpendicular
C	Midpoint
D	Coincident
E	Horizontal
F	Vertical
G	Colinear
H	Equal
I	Tangent
J	Concentric
K	Symmetric
L	At The Origin

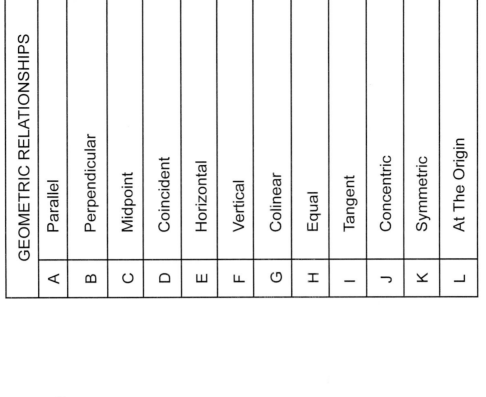
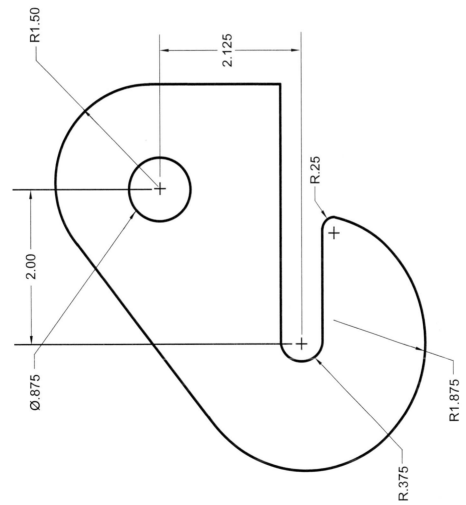

R1.50

2.125

Ø.875

2.00

R.25

R1.875

R.375

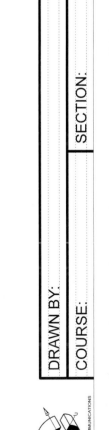

GRAPHIC COMMUNICATIONS

DRAWN BY:		TITLE:		GEO 110
COURSE:		SECTION:	SCALE:	DATE:

REV 2004

Label the geometric relationships found in the drawing with the appropriate letter to the RIGHT of the relationship.

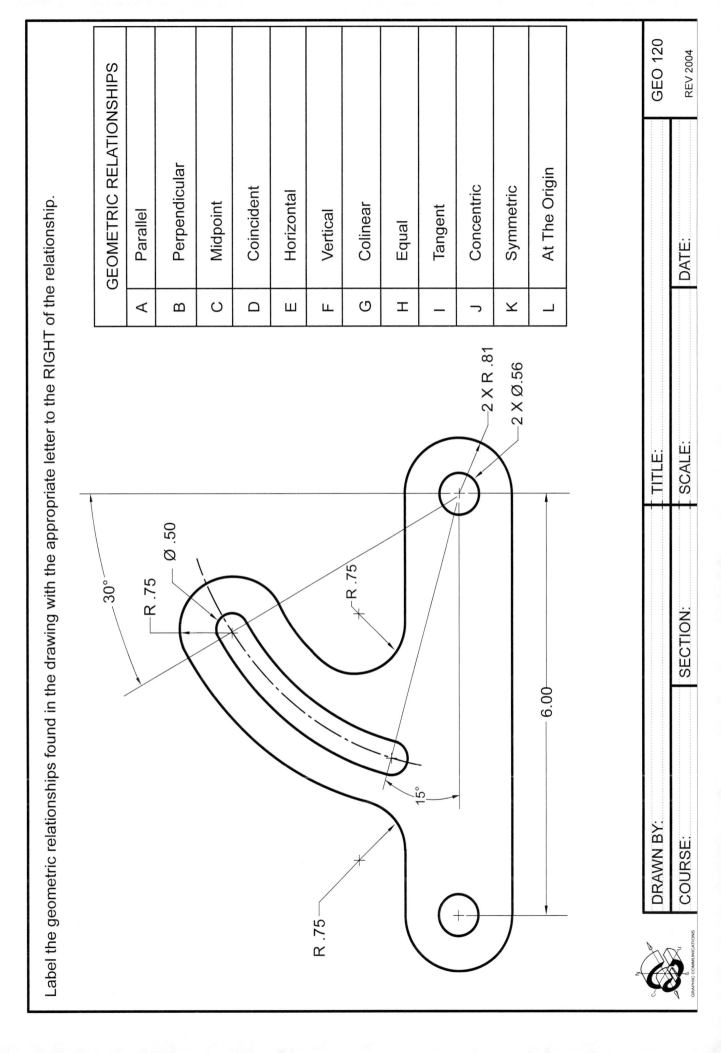

	GEOMETRIC RELATIONSHIPS
A	Parallel
B	Perpendicular
C	Midpoint
D	Coincident
E	Horizontal
F	Vertical
G	Colinear
H	Equal
I	Tangent
J	Concentric
K	Symmetric
L	At The Origin

2 X R .81
2 X Ø.56
30°
R .75
Ø .50
R .75
15°
6.00
R .75

GEO 120

REV 2004

GRAPHIC COMMUNICATIONS

DRAWN BY:		TITLE:	
COURSE:	SECTION:	SCALE:	DATE:

Modeling Procedure Worksheet

Fill in the table below with the appropriate information. The Feature Manager Design Tree has been provided below. The first row of the table has been completed for you.

Feature Name	Plane/Surface Selected	Sketch Figure	Feature/Sweep Type & End Condition	Resultant Model
Extrude 1	Horizontal Plane	F	Extruded Boss/Base Blind	C

Feature Manager Design Tree

A

B

C

D

E

F

G

H

Sketch the GASKET below at a drawing scale of 2:1.

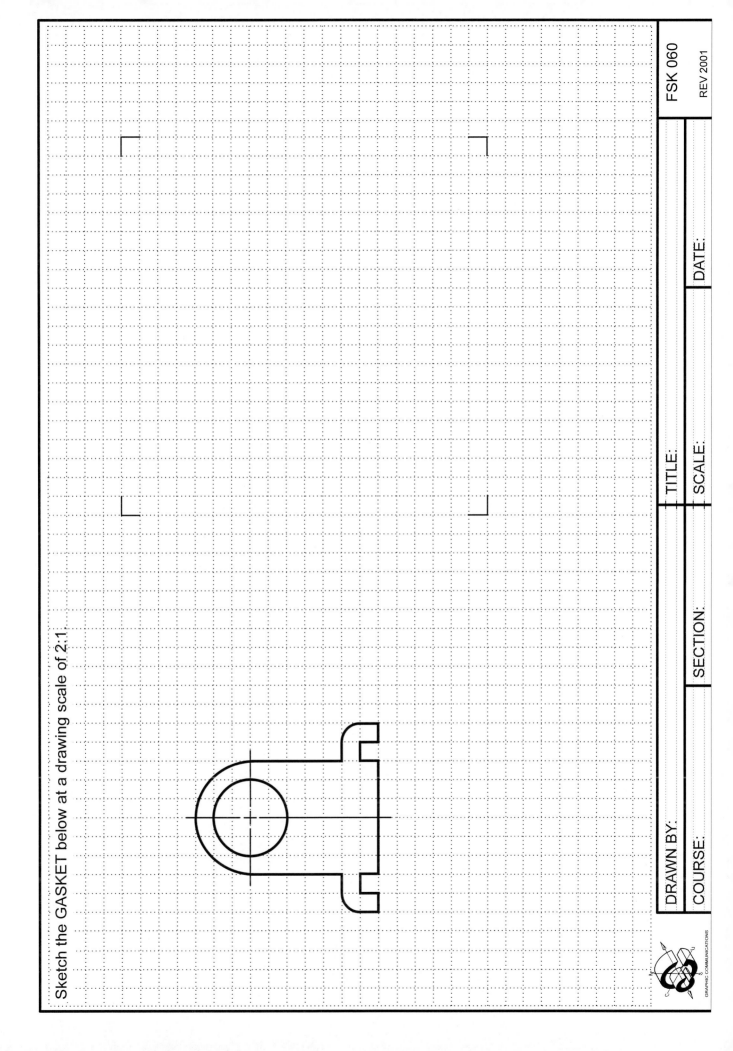

DRAWN BY:

COURSE:

TITLE:

SECTION:

SCALE:

DATE:

FSK 060

REV 2001

Sketch the CELTIC SQUARE in the grid below.
Each grid space represents 5mm.

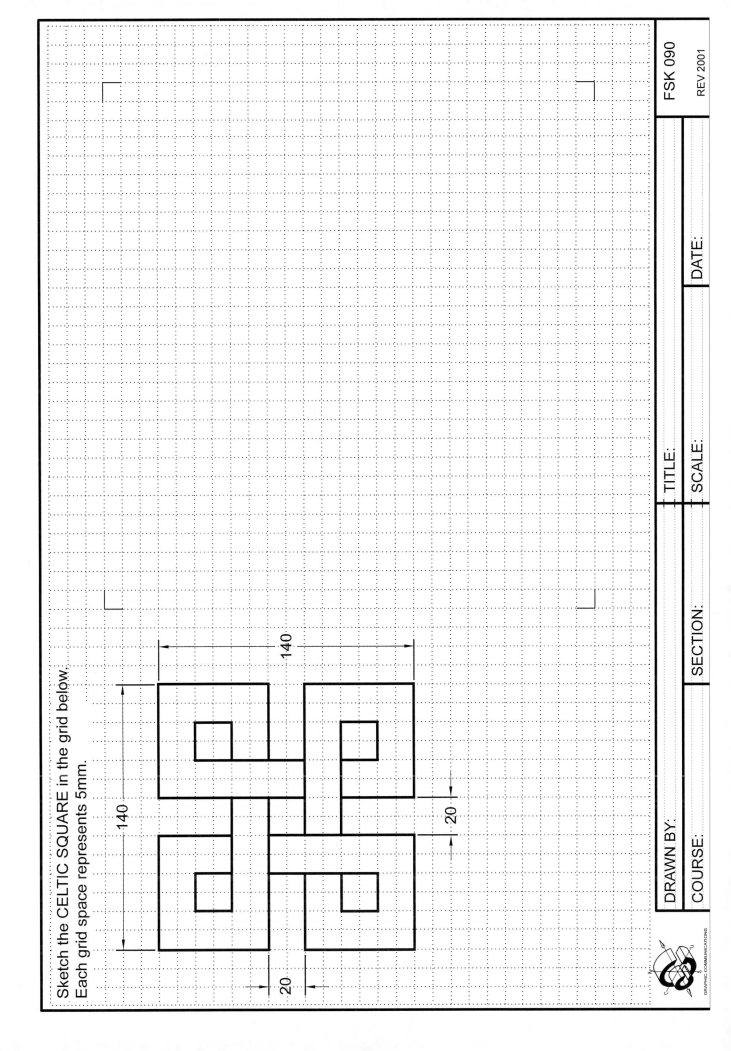

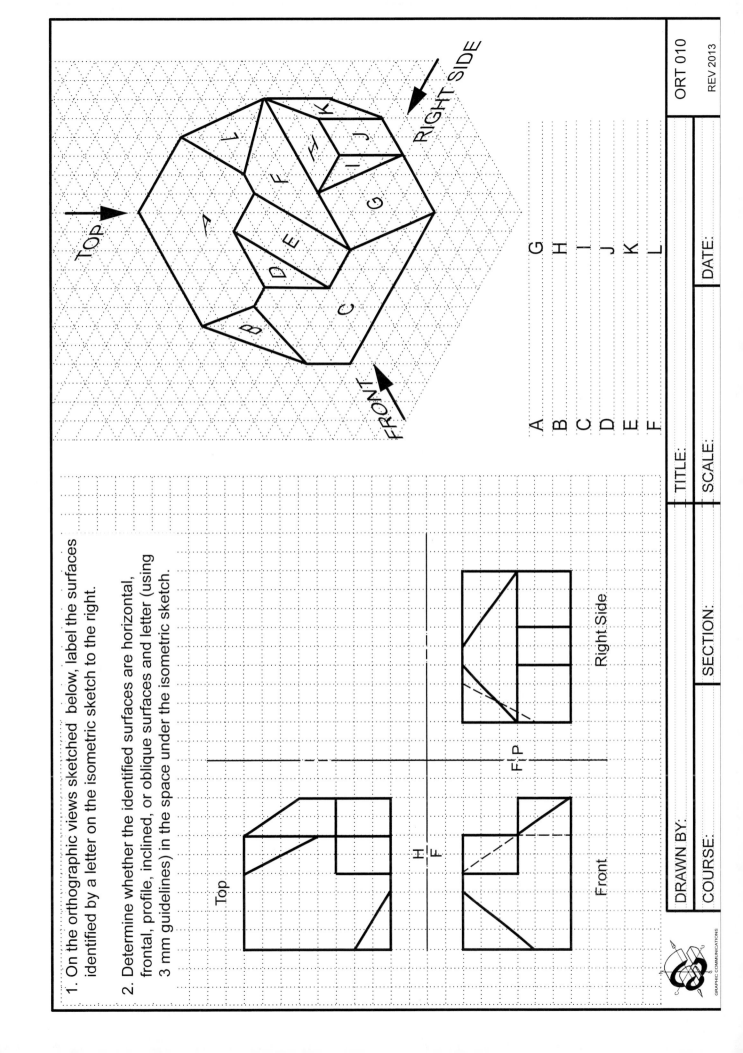

1. On the orthographic views sketched below, label the surfaces identified by a letter on the isometric sketch to the right.

2. Determine whether the identified surfaces are horizontal, frontal, profile, inclined, or oblique surfaces and letter (using 3 mm guidelines) in the space under the isometric sketch.

A .... G ....
B .... H ....
C .... I ....
D .... J ....
E .... K ....
F .... L ....

TOP

RIGHT SIDE

FRONT

Top.

H/F

F/P

Front.

Right Side.

ORT 010

REV 2013

GRAPHIC COMMUNICATIONS

DRAWN BY:

COURSE:

TITLE:

SCALE:

SECTION:

DATE:

For each one of the four problems, label the points in the three views as given in the pictorial.

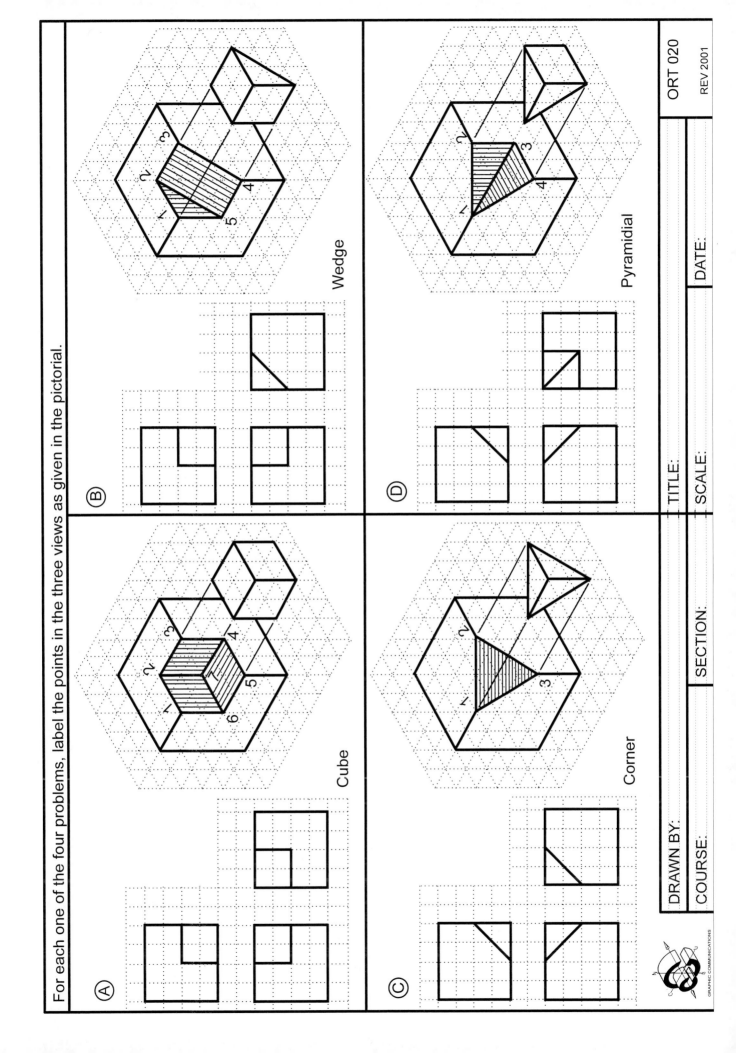

(A) Cube

(B) Wedge

(C) Corner

(D) Pyramidial

DRAWN BY:

COURSE:

TITLE:

SECTION:

SCALE:

DATE:

ORT 020

REV 2001

GRAPHIC COMMUNICATIONS

For each one of the four problems, label the points in the pictorial views as given in the three views.

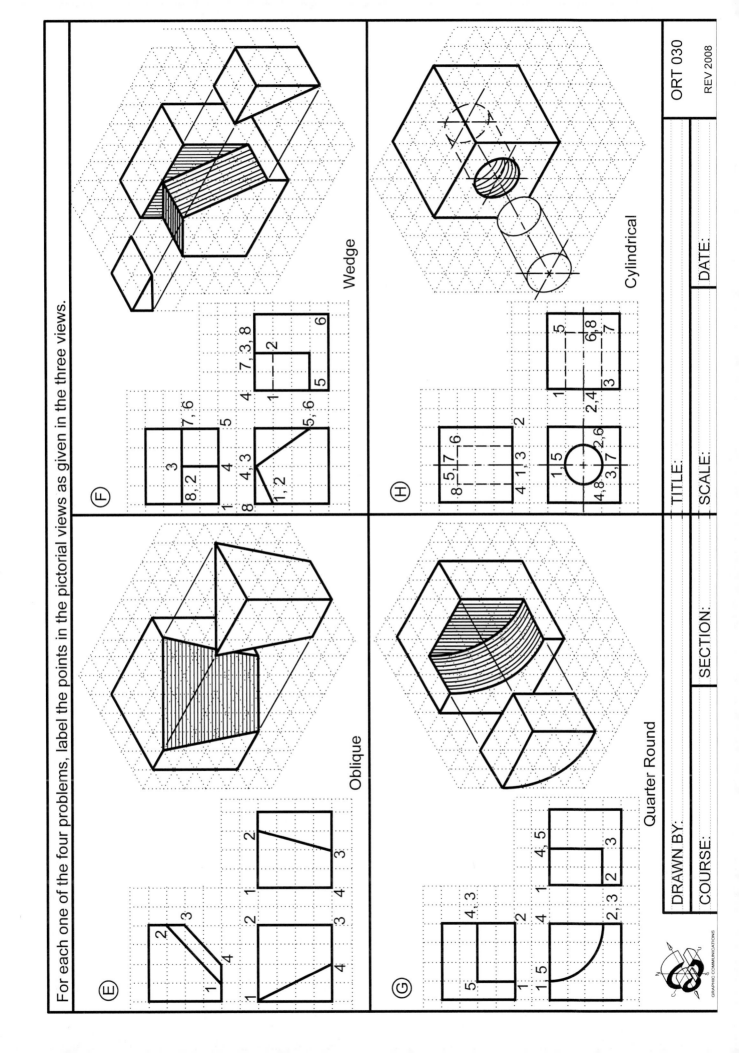

(E)

Oblique

(F)

Wedge

(G)

Quarter Round

(H)

Cylindrical

ORT 030

REV 2008

GRAPHIC COMMUNICATIONS

TITLE:

DATE:

DRAWN BY:

COURSE:

SECTION:

SCALE:

On the grids provided, sketch the designated views for each of the four objects.

Top, Front, Side

Top, Front, Side

Top, Front, Side

Top, Front, Side

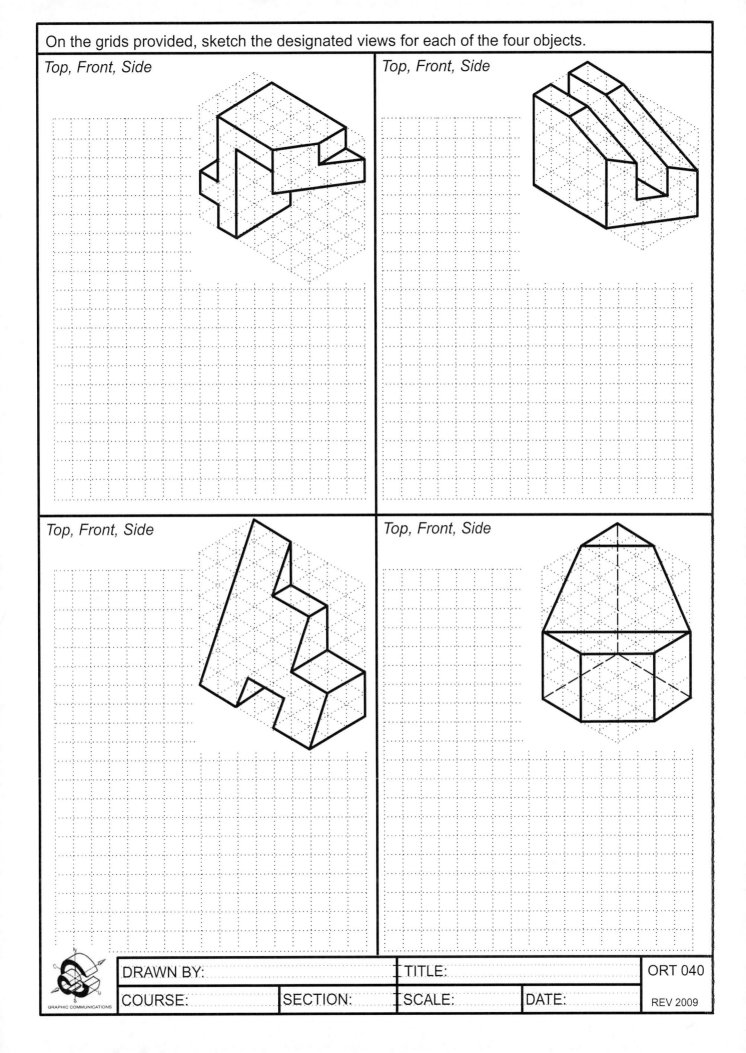

DRAWN BY:

TITLE:

ORT 040

COURSE:

SECTION:

SCALE:

DATE:

REV 2009

Neatly sketch top and right side views.
Do not dimension the drawing unless
specified by your instructor.

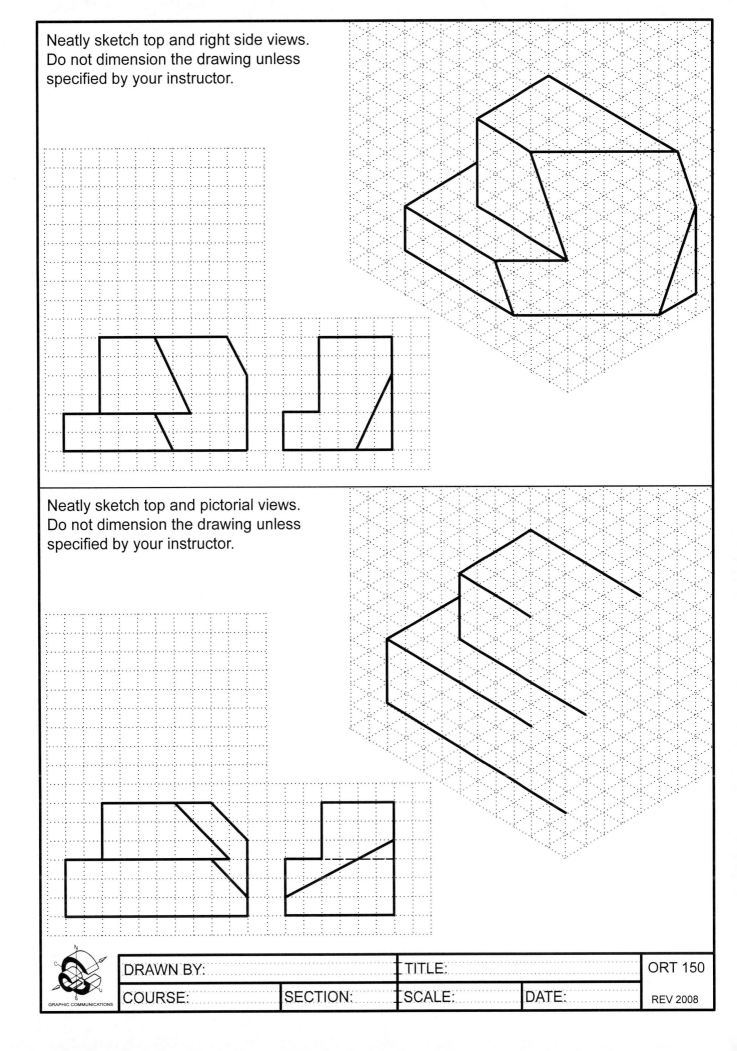

Neatly sketch top and pictorial views.
Do not dimension the drawing unless
specified by your instructor.

On the grids provided, sketch the designated views for each of the four objects.

Top, Front, Side

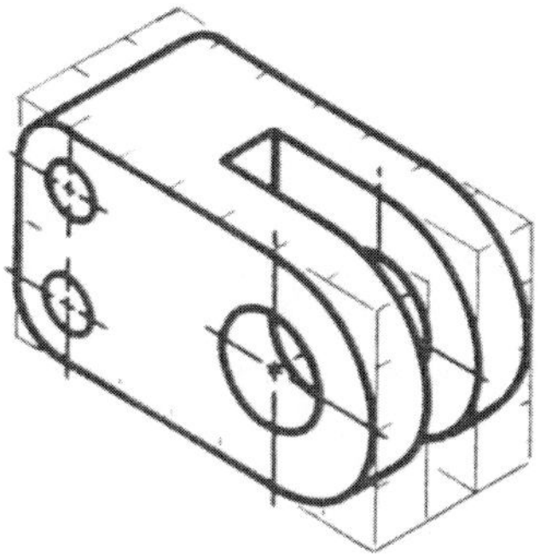

Top, Front, Side

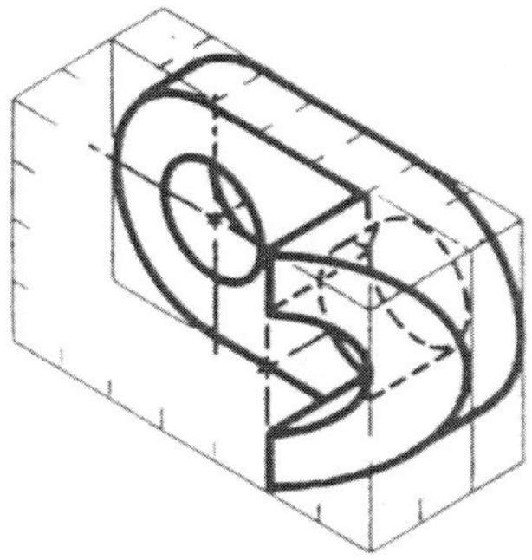

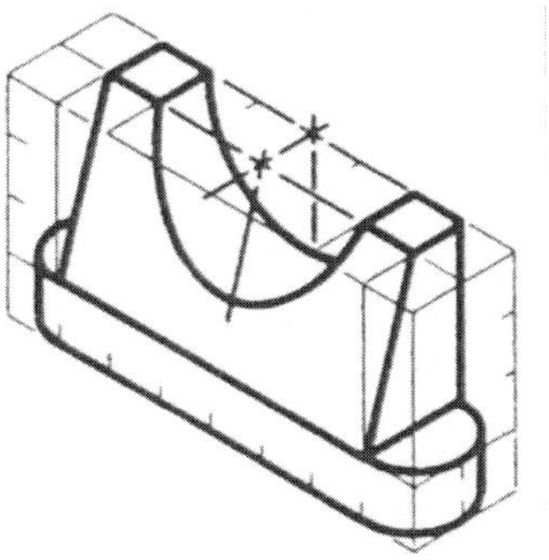

Top, Front, Side

Front, Side

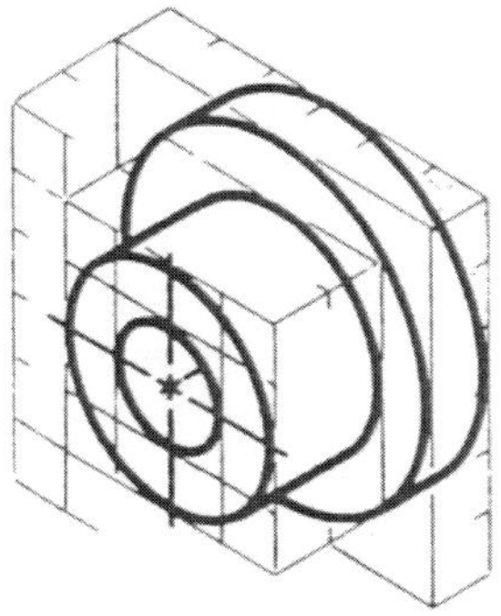

DRAWN BY:		TITLE:		ORT 050
COURSE:	SECTION:	SCALE:	DATE:	REV 2009

GRAPHIC COMMUNICATIONS

In each of the ten problems below you are given a pictorial of an object and an arrow indicating the view (top, front, or right side). Select the correct view (A, B, C or D) indicated by the arrow and lace the identifying letter in the answer space on the right.

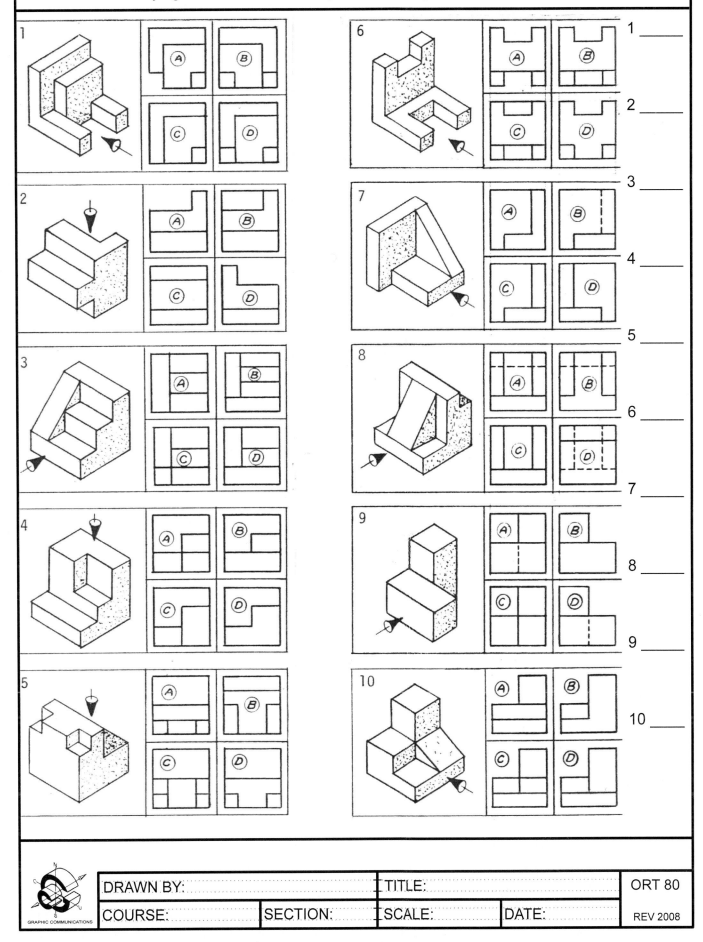

1 _____

2 _____

3 _____

4 _____

5 _____

6 _____

7 _____

8 _____

9 _____

10 _____

GRAPHIC COMMUNICATIONS

DRAWN BY:

COURSE:

SECTION:

TITLE:

SCALE:

DATE:

ORT 80

REV 2008

Select the right side view (or views where indicated as a choice) which could be used with the given top and front view in each problem. Place the identifying letter in the anser space on the right.

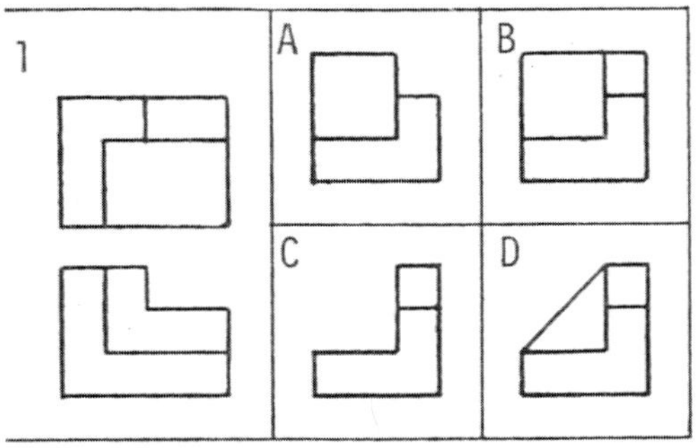

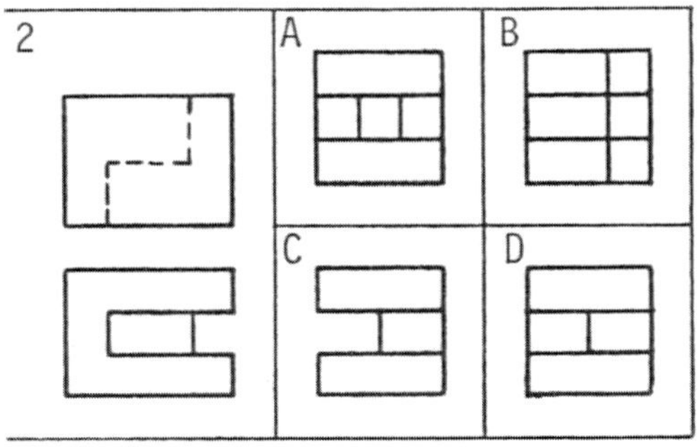

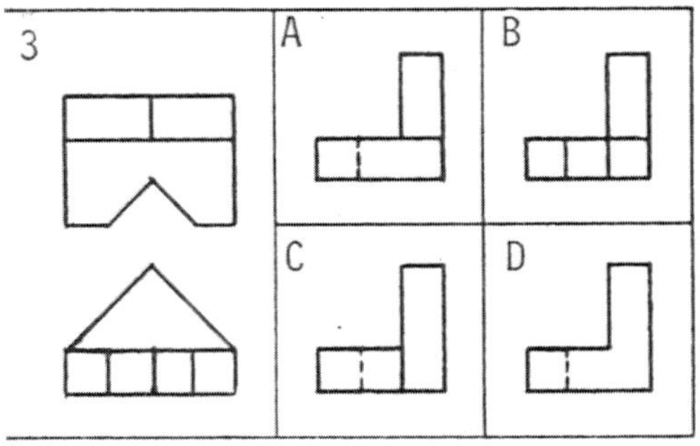

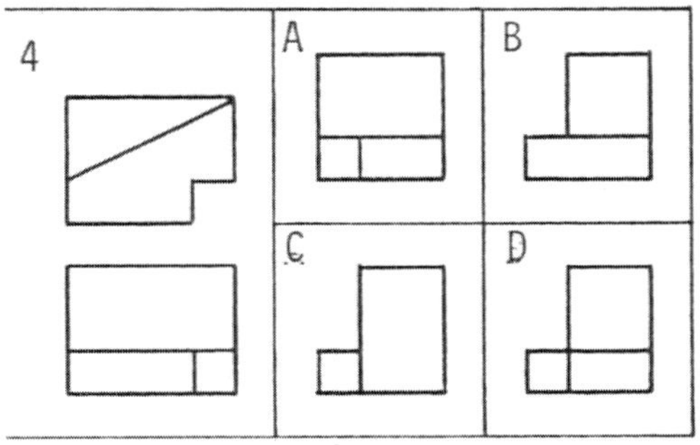

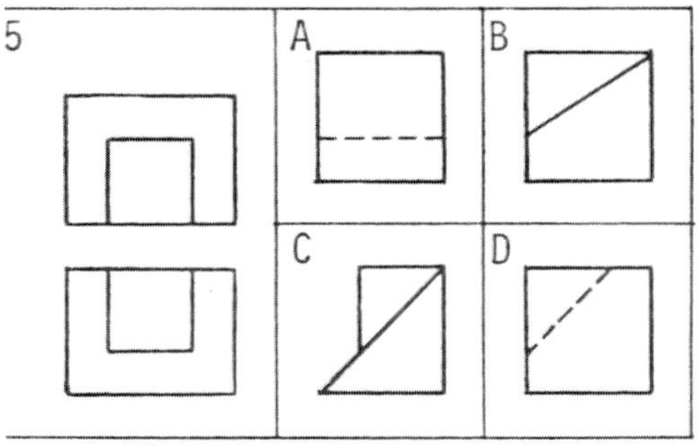

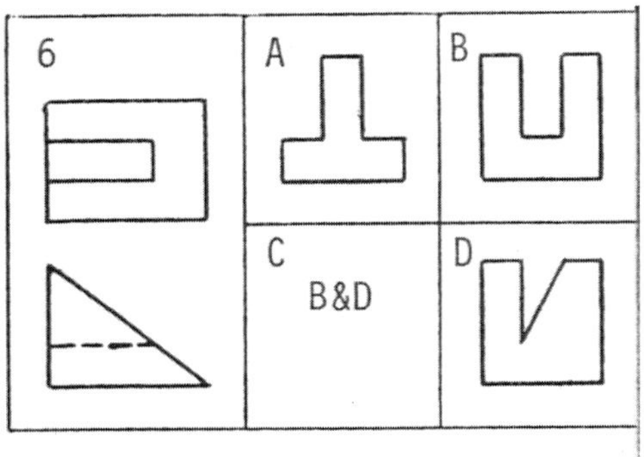

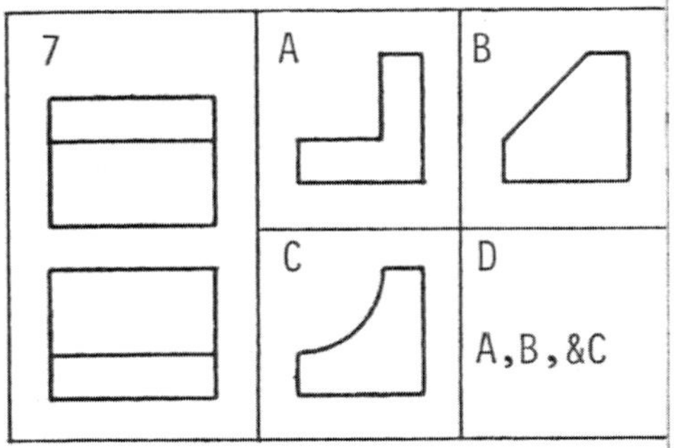

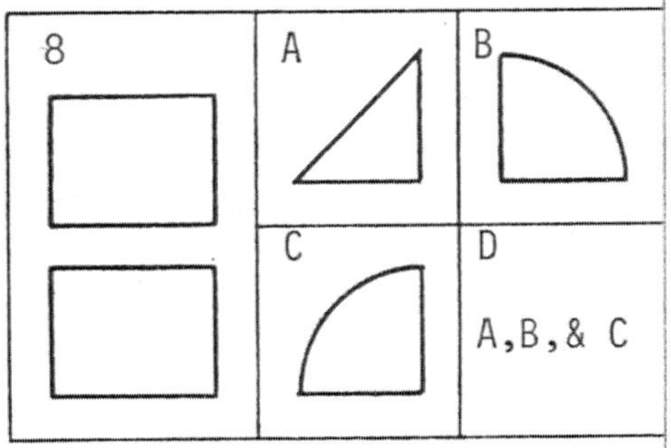

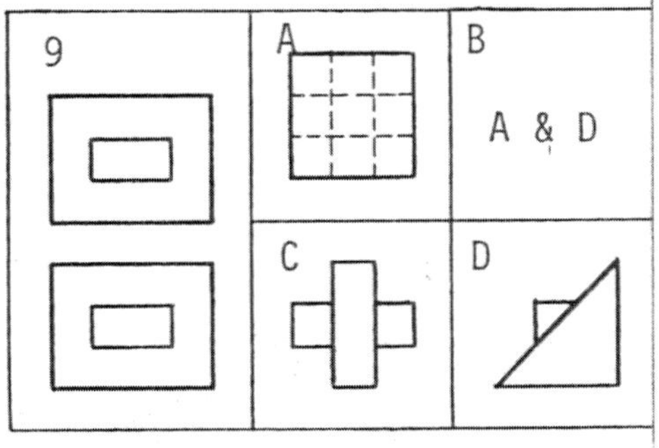

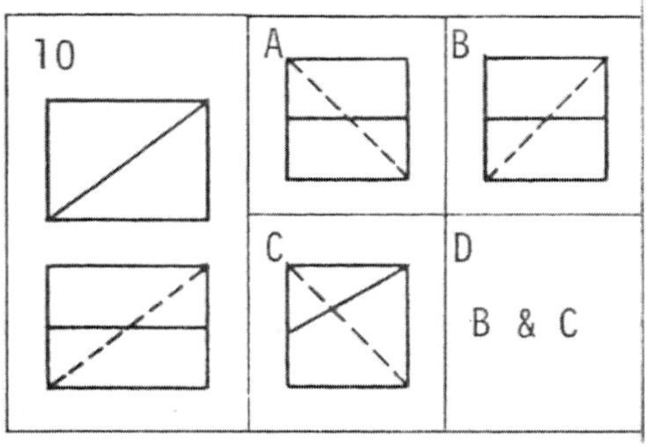

Problem 1

A   B
C   D

Problem 6

A   B
C   (B&D)   D

Problem 2

A   B
C   D

Problem 7

A   B
C   D (A,B,&C)

Problem 3

A   B
C   D

Problem 8

A   B
C   D (A,B,& C)

Problem 4

A   B
C   D

Problem 9

A   B (A & D)
C   D

Problem 5

A   B
C   D

Problem 10

A   B
C   D (B & C)

1 _____

2 _____

3 _____

4 _____

5 _____

6 _____

7 _____

8 _____

9 _____

10 _____

DRAWN BY:
COURSE: SECTION: SCALE: DATE:
TITLE:
ORT 90
REV 2008
GRAPHIC COMMUNICATIONS

In the problems below you are given two complete views. One view is incomplete.
Sketch the missing line or lines to make the partial view complete.
Draw/sketch isometric pictorials of problems: ______________________

1
2
3
4
5
6
7
8
9
10
11
12
13
14
15
16
17
18
19
20

GRAPHIC COMMUNICATIONS

DRAWN BY:		TITLE:		ORT 100
COURSE:	SECTION:	SCALE:	DATE:	REV 2008

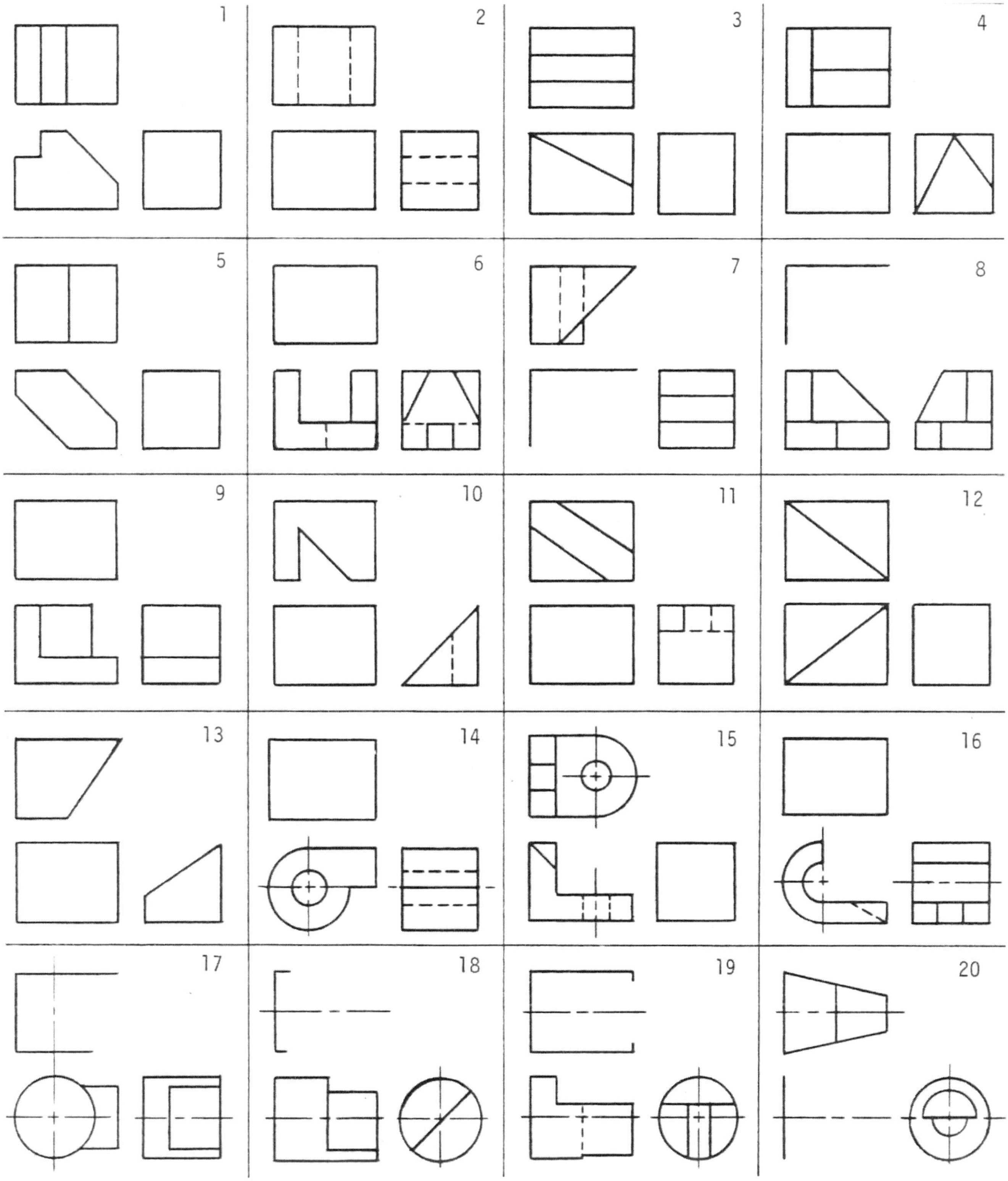

In the problems below sketch the missing line or lines to make the partial views complete.

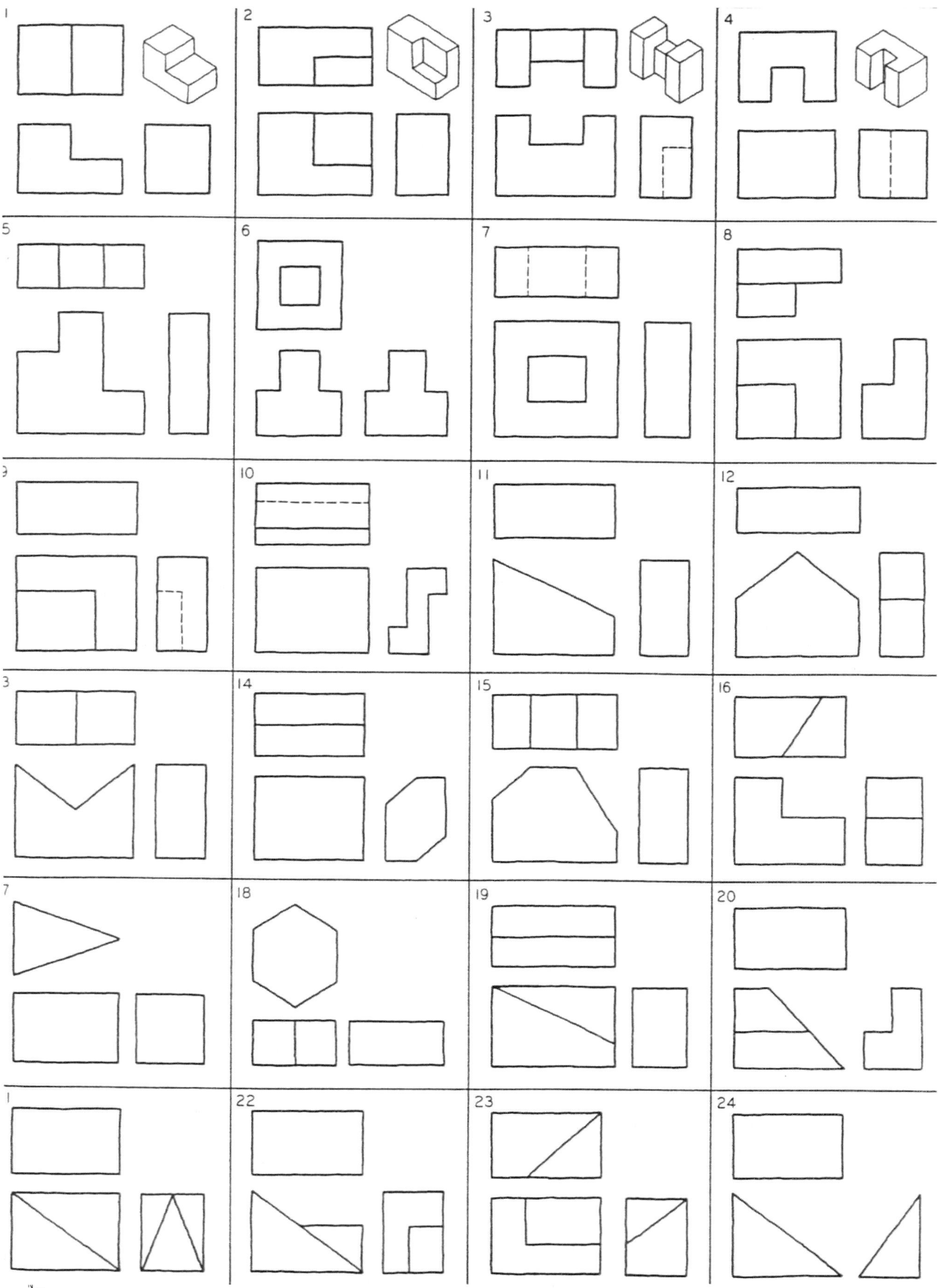

1

2

3

4

5

6

7

8

9

10

11

12

3

14

15

16

7

18

19

20

1

22

23

24

DRAWN BY:

TITLE:

ORT 105

COURSE:

SECTION:

SCALE:

DATE:

REV 2008

GRAPHIC COMMUNICATIONS

In the problems below you are given two complete views. One view is incomplete.
Sketch the missing line or lines to make the partial view complete.
Draw/sketch isometric pictorials of problems: ____________________________________

1
2
3
4
5
6
7
8
9
10
11
12
13
14
15
16
17
18
19
20

GRAPHIC COMMUNICATIONS

DRAWN BY:		TITLE:		ORT 110
COURSE:	SECTION:	SCALE:	DATE:	REV 2008

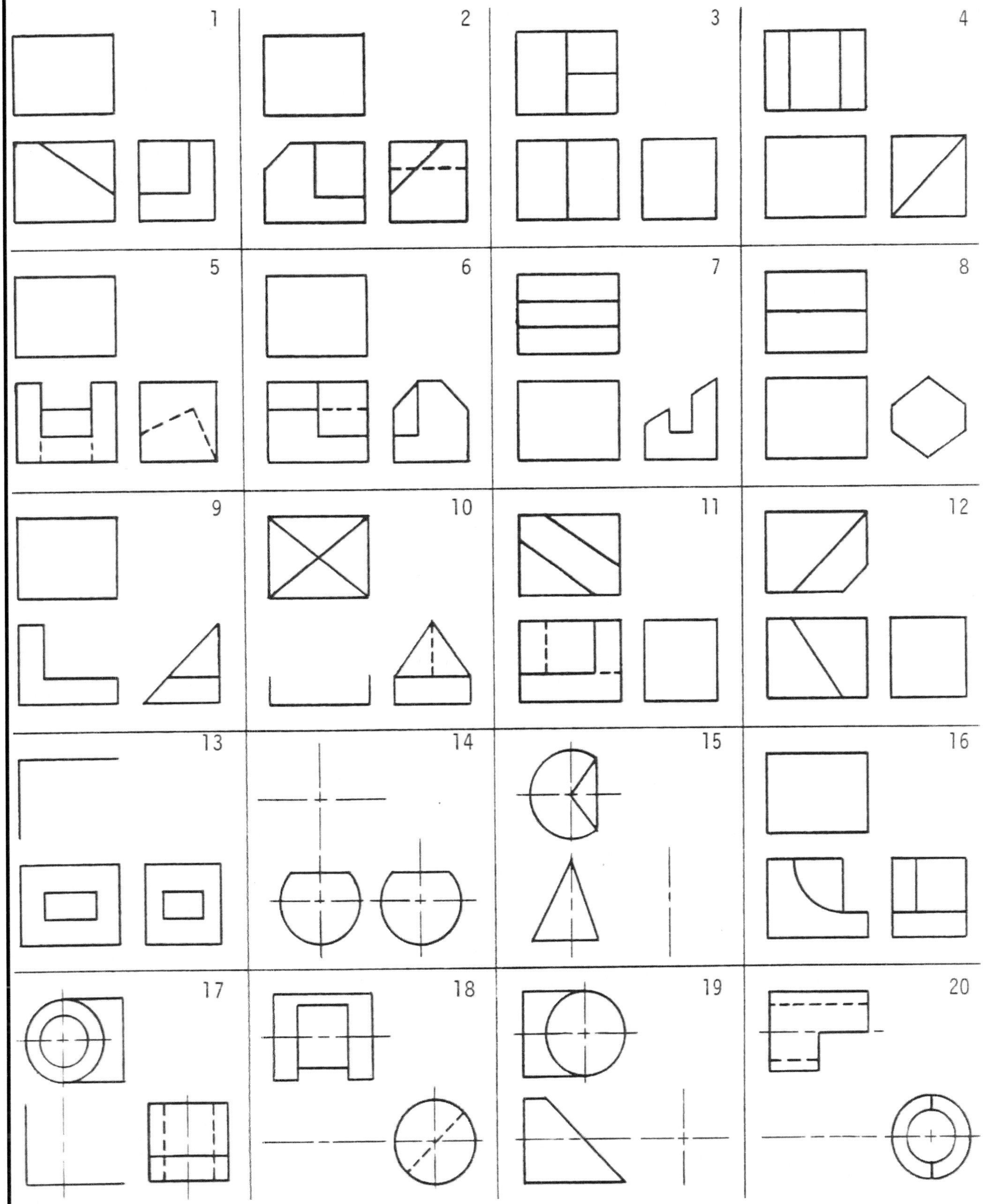

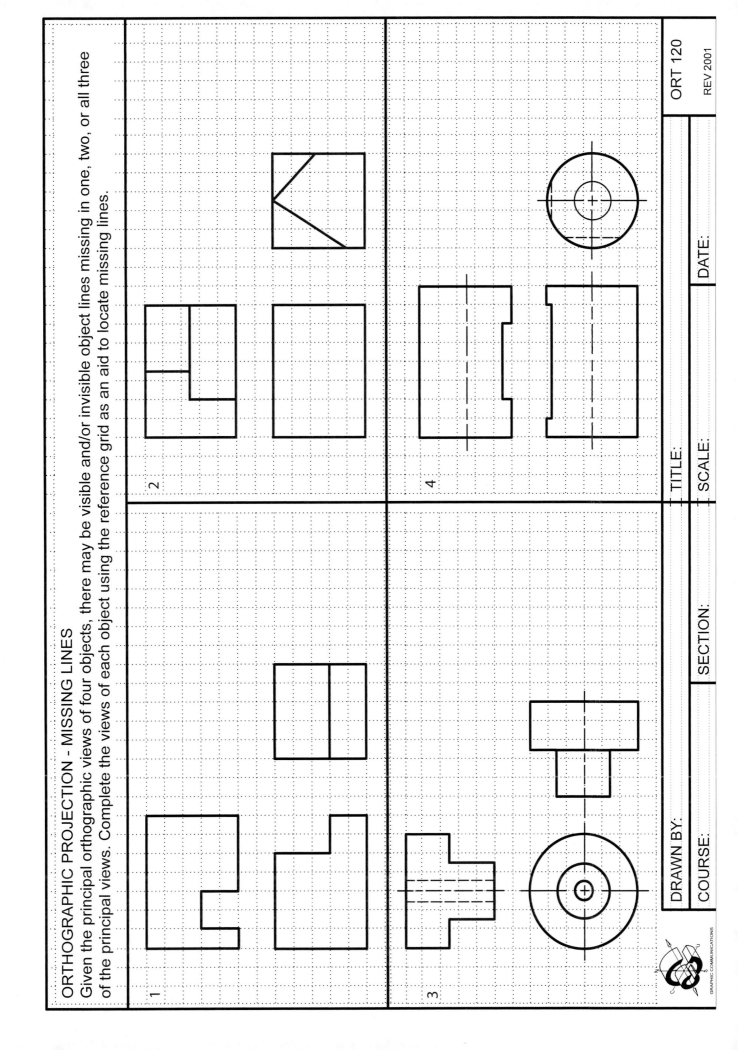

ORTHOGRAPHIC PROJECTION - MISSING LINES

Given the principal orthographic views of four objects, there may be visible and/or invisible object lines missing in one, two, or all three of the principal views. Complete the views of each object using the reference grid as an aid to locate missing lines.

1

2

3

4

DRAWN BY:		SECTION:	ORT 120
COURSE:			REV 2001
TITLE:			
SCALE:	DATE:		

ORTHOGRAPHIC PROJECTION - MISSING VIEWS

Two complete principal orthographic views are given for each of the four objects shown below.
Draw the missing principal view of each object.

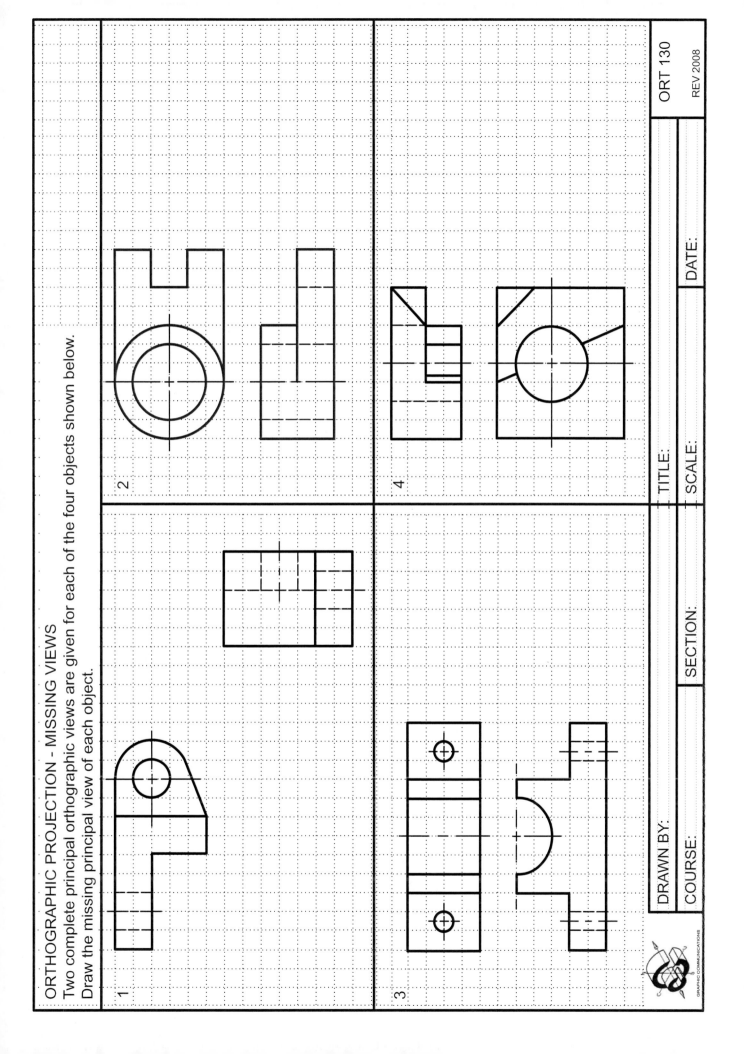

1

2

3

4

ORT 130

REV 2008

GRAPHIC COMMUNICATIONS

DRAWN BY:

COURSE:

SECTION:

TITLE:

SCALE:

DATE:

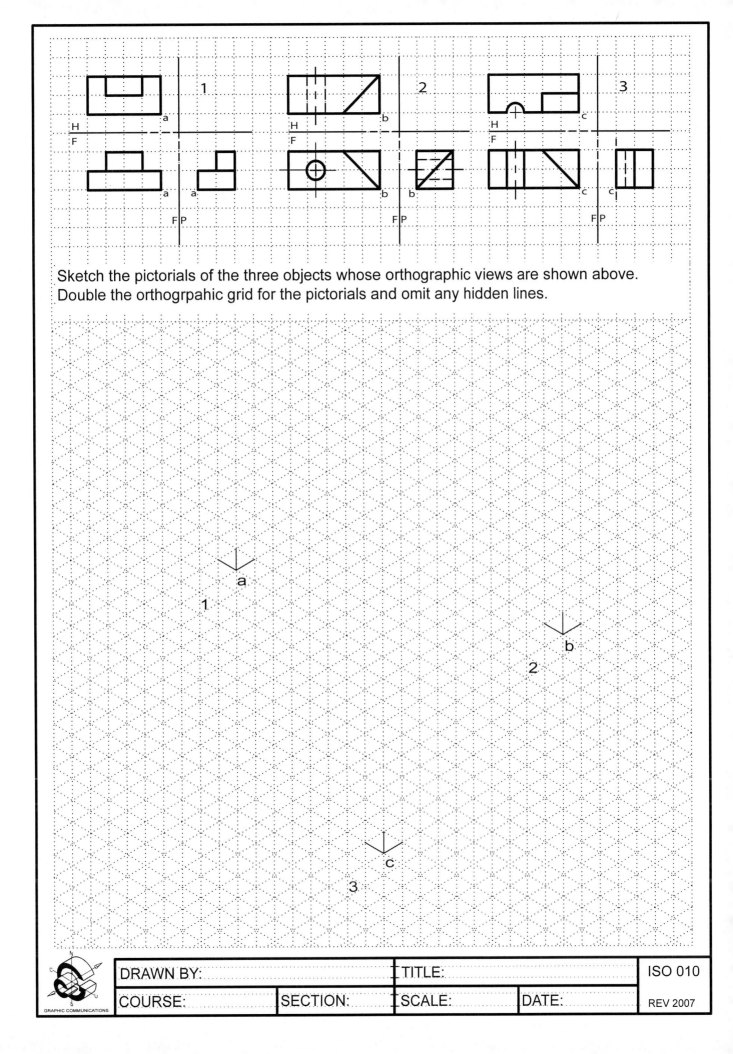

Sketch the pictorials of the three objects whose orthographic views are shown above.
Double the orthogrpahic grid for the pictorials and omit any hidden lines.

DRAWN BY:

TITLE:

ISO 010

COURSE:

SECTION:

SCALE:

DATE:

REV 2007

GRAPHIC COMMUNICATIONS

From the provided multiviews sketch the
pictorial-omit hidden lines.

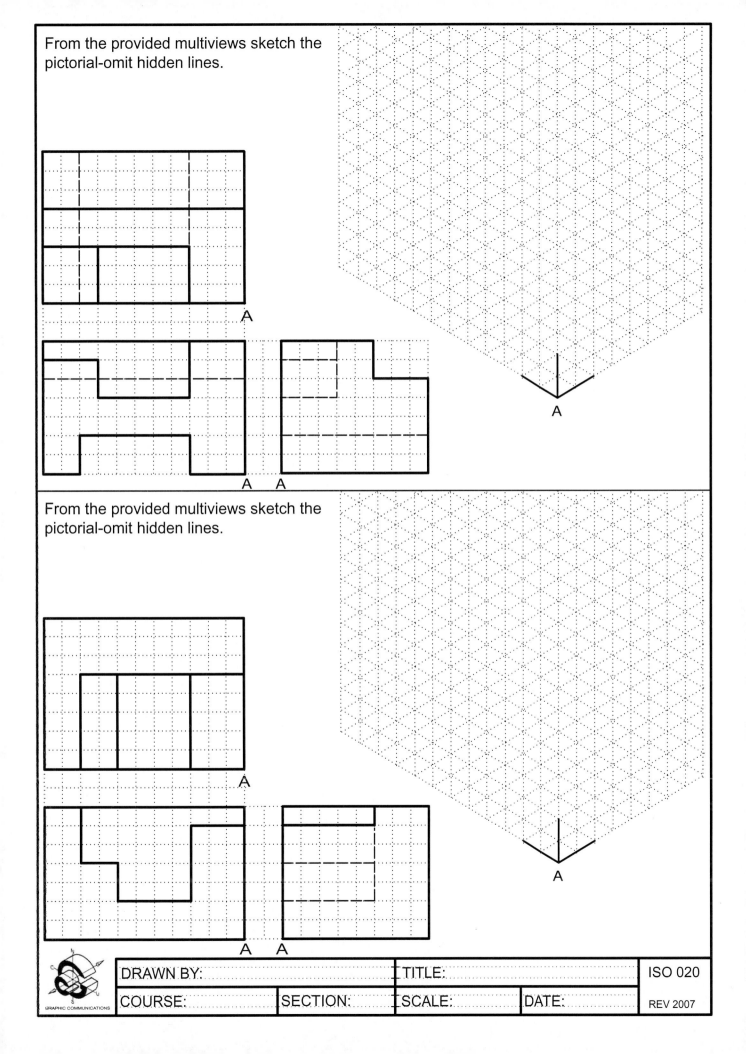

From the provided multiviews sketch the
pictorial-omit hidden lines.

Make a full-size isometric drawing of each
object in the space provided. Start corner
A as shown.

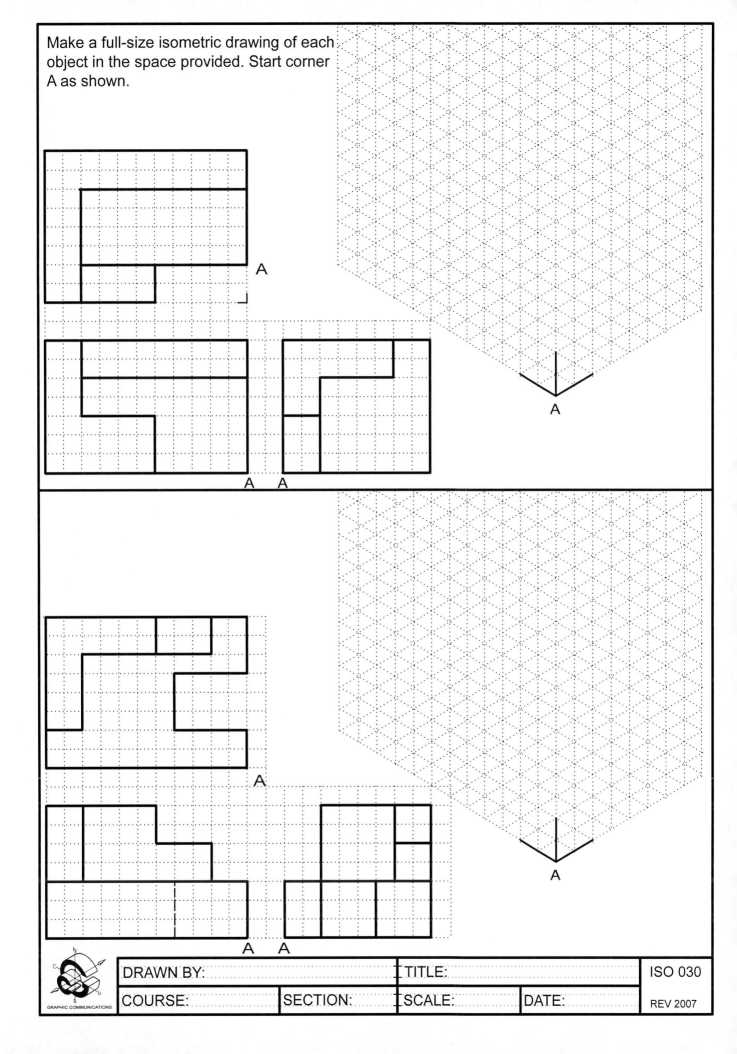

ISO 030

REV 2007

DRAWN BY:

TITLE:

COURSE:

SECTION:

SCALE:

DATE:

GRAPHIC COMMUNICATIONS

Make a full-size isometric drawing of each object in the space provided. Start corner A as shown.

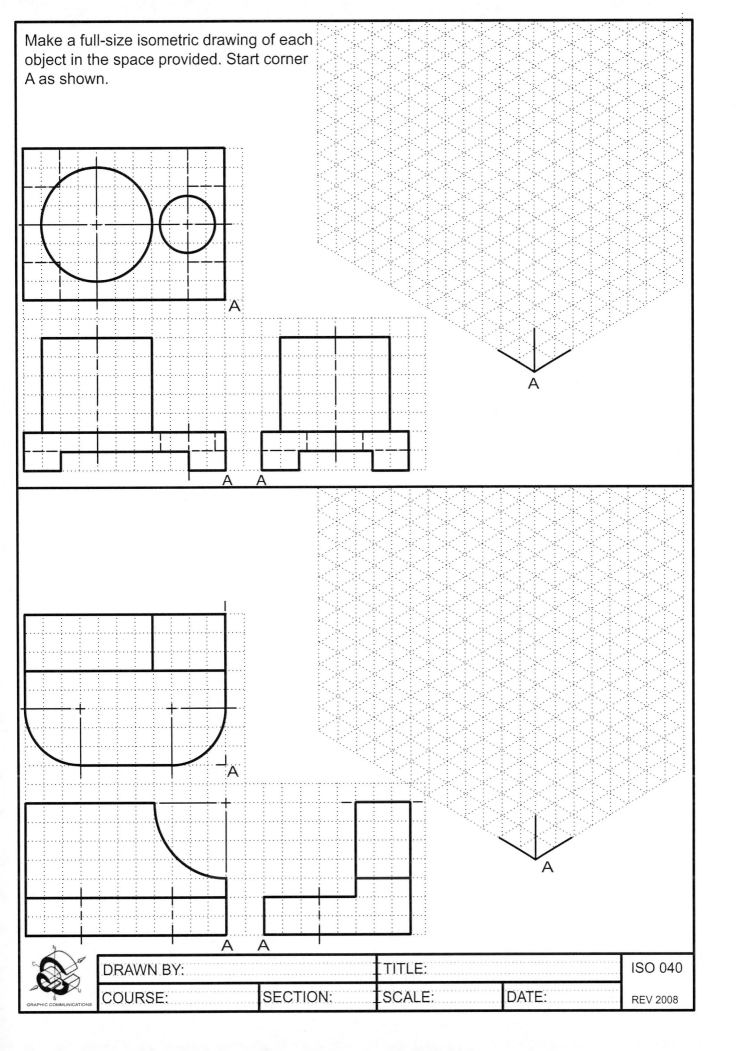

DRAWN BY:		TITLE:		ISO 040
COURSE:	SECTION:	SCALE:	DATE:	REV 2008

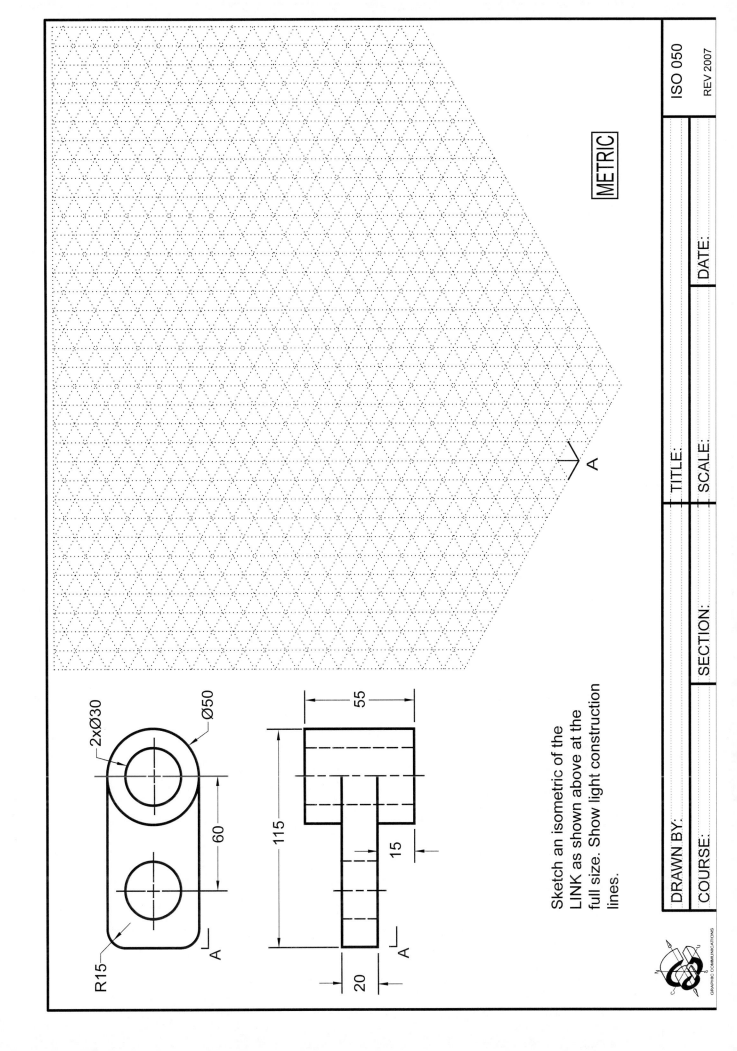

2xØ30

Ø50

R15

60

A

A

55

115

15

20

A

A

Sketch an isometric of the
LINK as shown above at the
full size. Show light construction
lines.

DRAWN BY:

COURSE:

TITLE:

SECTION:

SCALE:

DATE:

METRIC

ISO 050

REV 2007

Draw the missing front view in full section. A pictorial of the section is shown to assist you. Indicate the cutting-plane in the appropriate view. NOTE: Refer to the text for the correct line symbol for a cutting-plane line and for correct arrowheads.

Draw the missing front view as an offset section. Indicate the cutting-plane in the appropriate view. NOTE: Refer to the text for the correct line symbol for a cutting-plane line and for correct arrowheads.

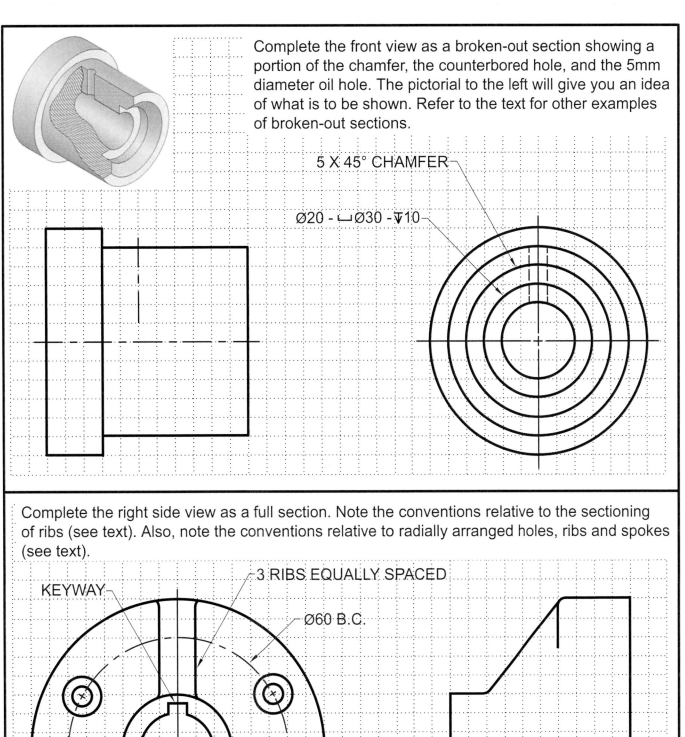

Complete the front view as a broken-out section showing a portion of the chamfer, the counterbored hole, and the 5mm diameter oil hole. The pictorial to the left will give you an idea of what is to be shown. Refer to the text for other examples of broken-out sections.

5 X 45° CHAMFER

Ø20 - ⌴Ø30 - ▼10

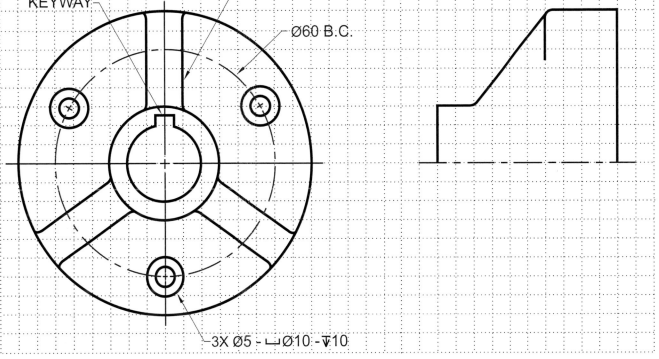

Complete the right side view as a full section. Note the conventions relative to the sectioning of ribs (see text). Also, note the conventions relative to radially arranged holes, ribs and spokes (see text).

KEYWAY

3 RIBS EQUALLY SPACED

Ø60 B.C.

3X Ø5 - ⌴Ø10 - ▼10

DRAWN BY:		TITLE:		SEC 020
COURSE:	SECTION:	SCALE:	DATE:	REV 2009

GRAPHIC COMMUNICATIONS

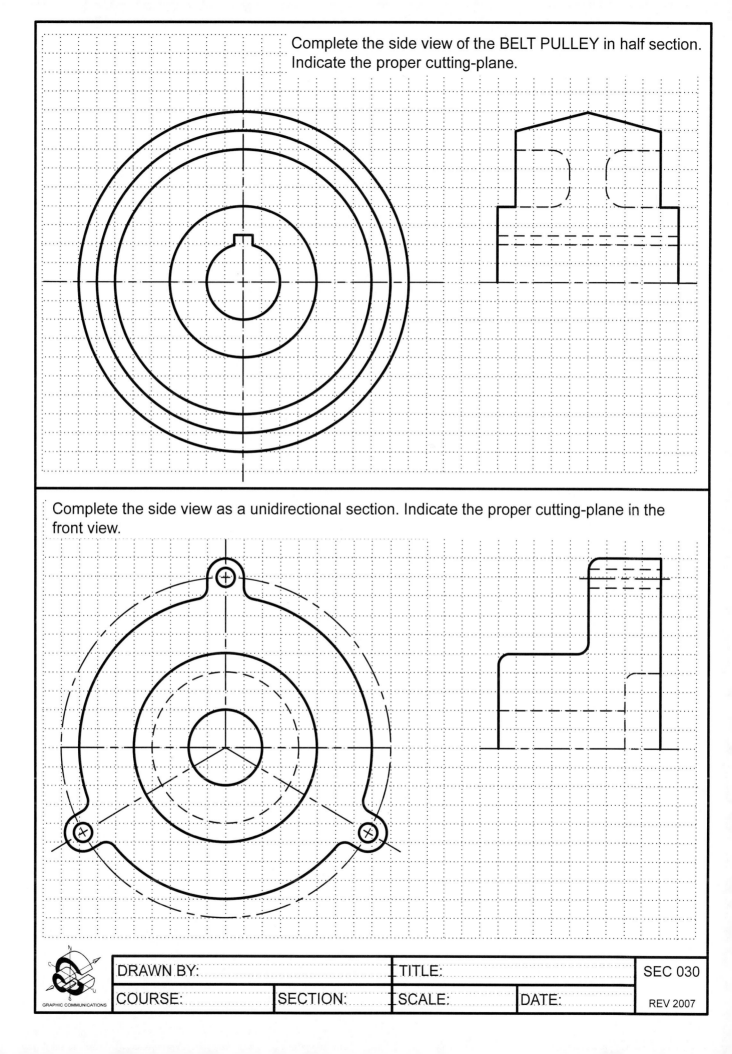

Complete the side view of the BELT PULLEY in half section. Indicate the proper cutting-plane.

Complete the side view as a unidirectional section. Indicate the proper cutting-plane in the front view.

DRAWN BY:

TITLE:

SEC 030

COURSE:

SECTION:

SCALE:

DATE:

REV 2007

GRAPHIC COMMUNICATIONS

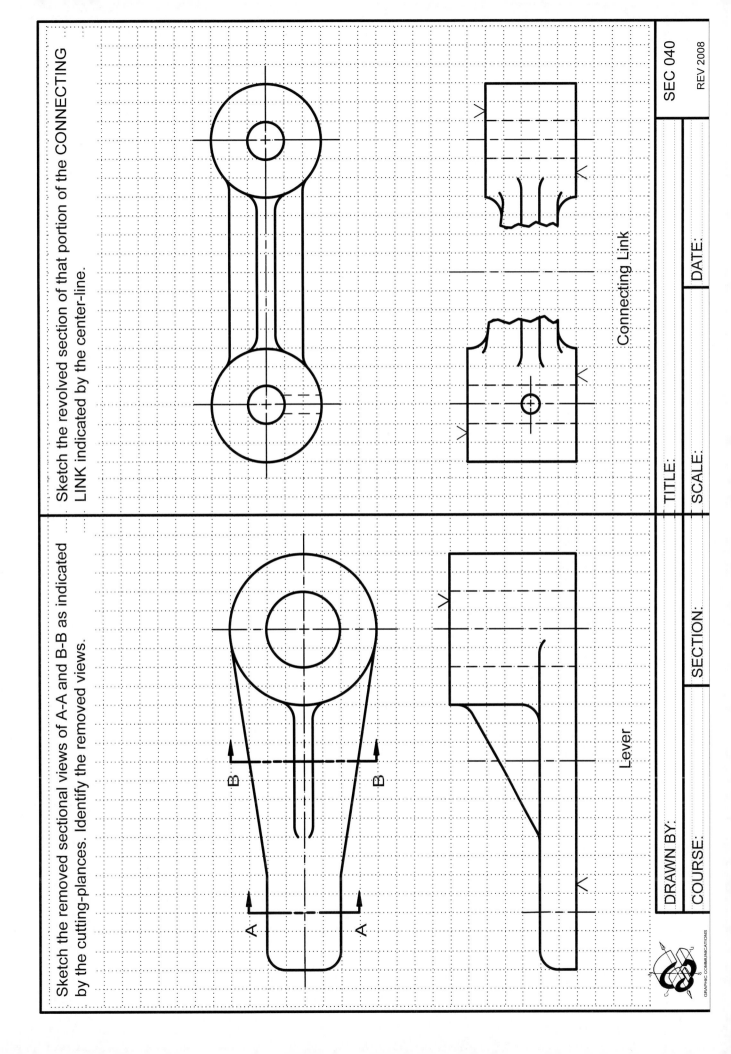

Sketch the revolved section of that portion of the CONNECTING LINK indicated by the center-line.

Connecting Link

Sketch the removed sectional views of A-A and B-B as indicated by the cutting-plances. Identify the removed views.

Lever

DRAWN BY:

COURSE:

SECTION:

TITLE:

SCALE:

DATE:

SEC 040

REV 2008

GRAPHIC COMMUNICATIONS

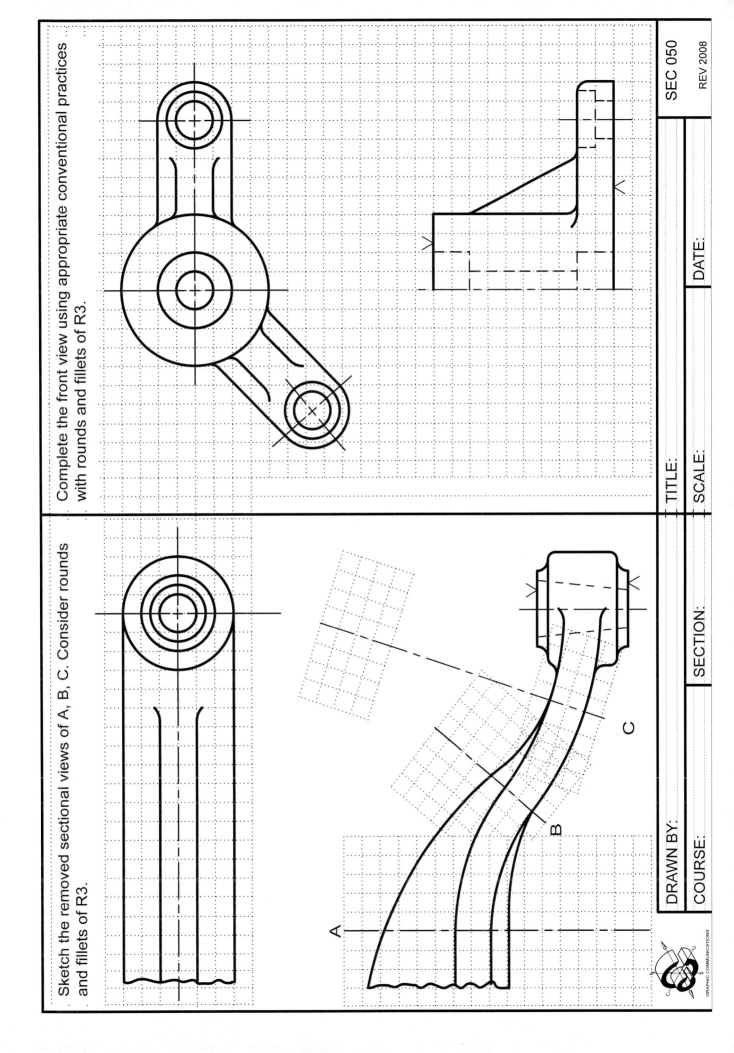

Complete the front view using appropriate conventional practices with rounds and fillets of R3.

Sketch the removed sectional views of A, B, C. Consider rounds and fillets of R3.

TITLE:

DATE:

SCALE:

SEC 050

REV 2008

DRAWN BY:

COURSE:

SECTION:

GRAPHIC COMMUNICATIONS

A

B

C

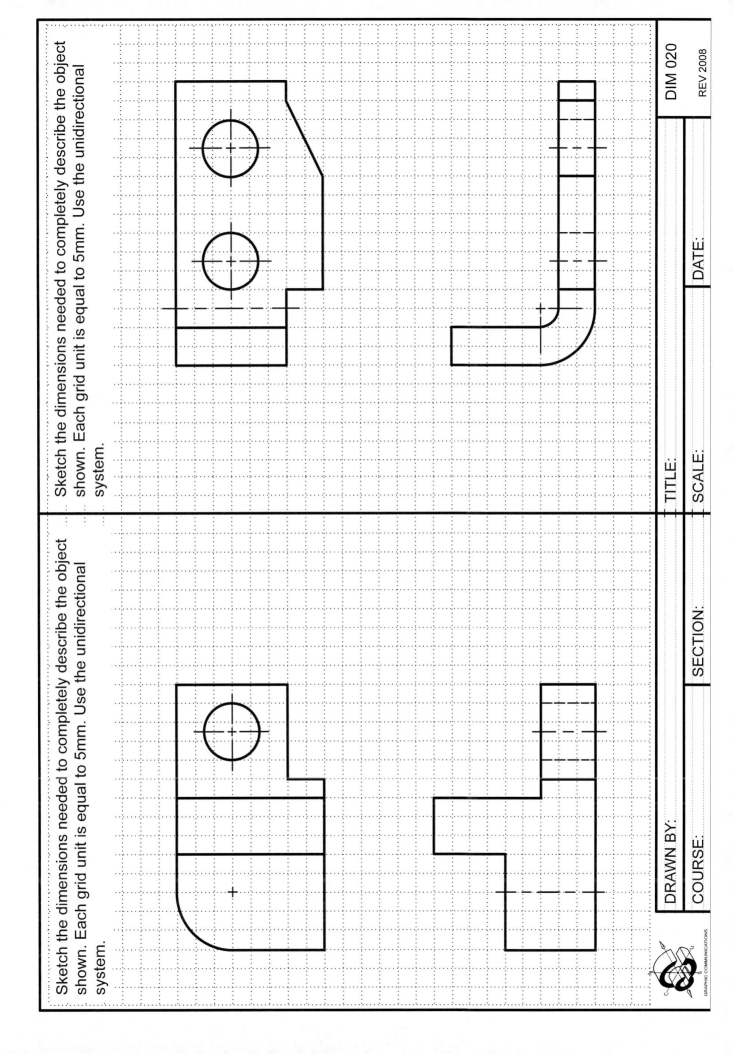

Sketch the dimensions needed to completely describe the object shown. Each grid unit is equal to 5mm. Use the unidirectional system.

Sketch the dimensions needed to completely describe the object shown. Each grid unit is equal to 5mm. Use the unidirectional system.

DIM 020

REV 2008

TITLE:

DATE:

SCALE:

DRAWN BY:

COURSE:

SECTION:

GRAPHIC COMMUNICATIONS

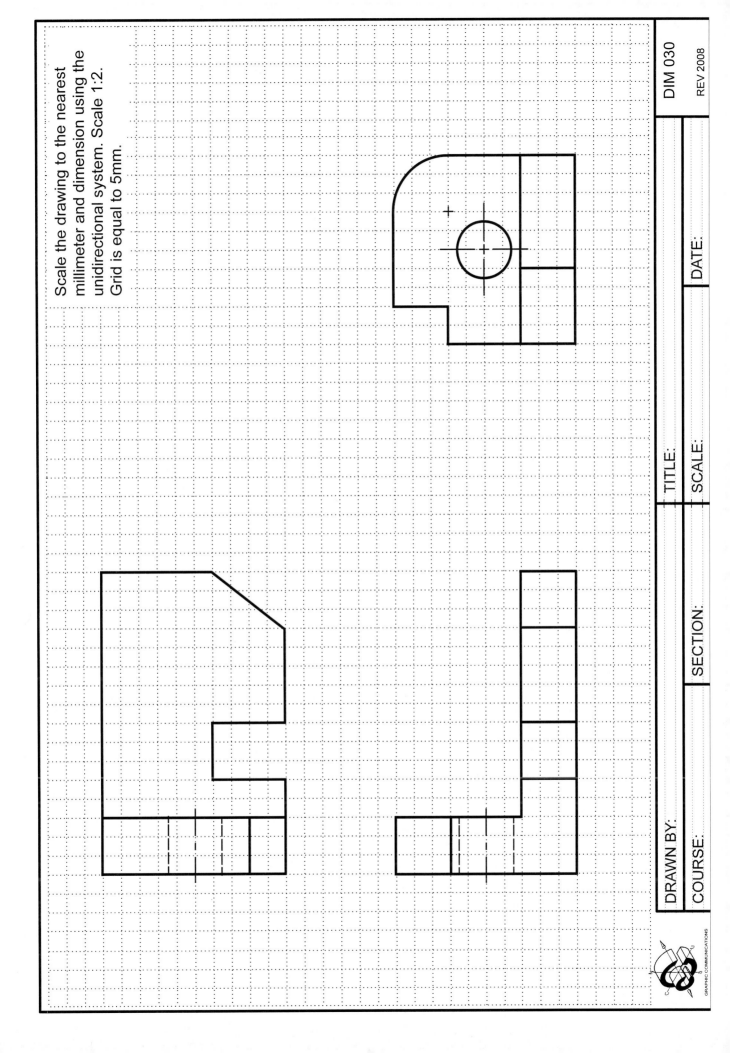

Scale the drawing to the nearest
millimeter and dimension using the
unidirectional system. Scale 1:2.
Grid is equal to 5mm.

DIM 030

REV 2008

TITLE:

SCALE:

DATE:

SECTION:

DRAWN BY:

COURSE:

GRAPHIC COMMUNICATIONS

Using the unidirectional system, dimension the
bushing using full scale. Estimate all sizes.

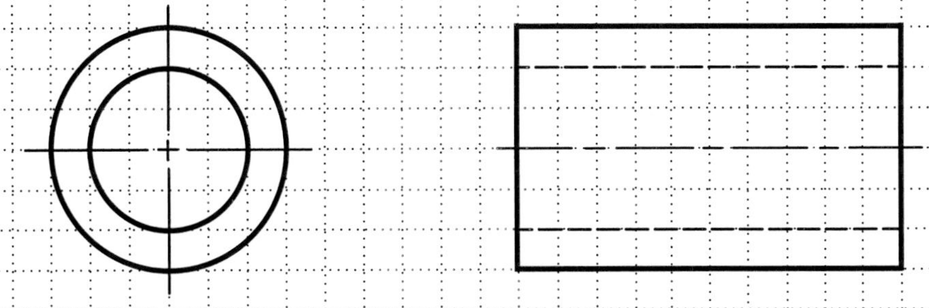

Using the unidirectional system, dimension the
plug shown using a scale of 1:3. Estimate all sizes.

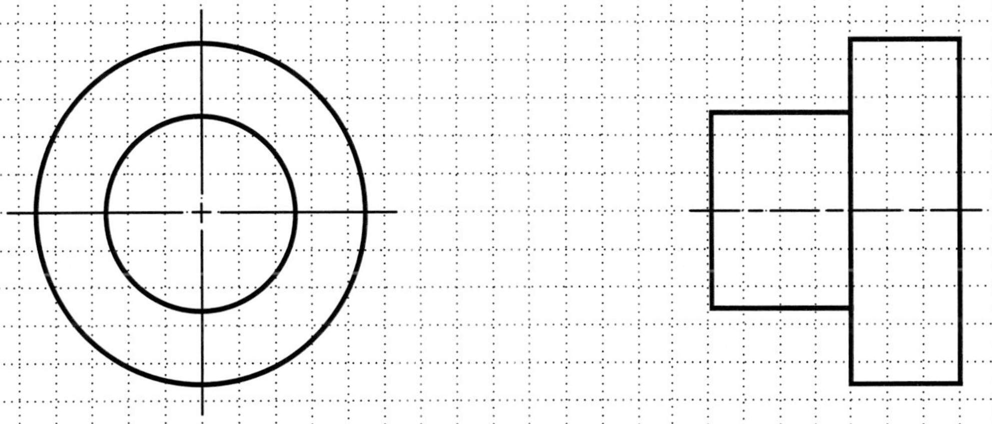

DRAWN BY:

COURSE:

SECTION:

TITLE:

SCALE:

DATE:

DIM 040

REV 2008

GRAPHIC COMMUNICATIONS

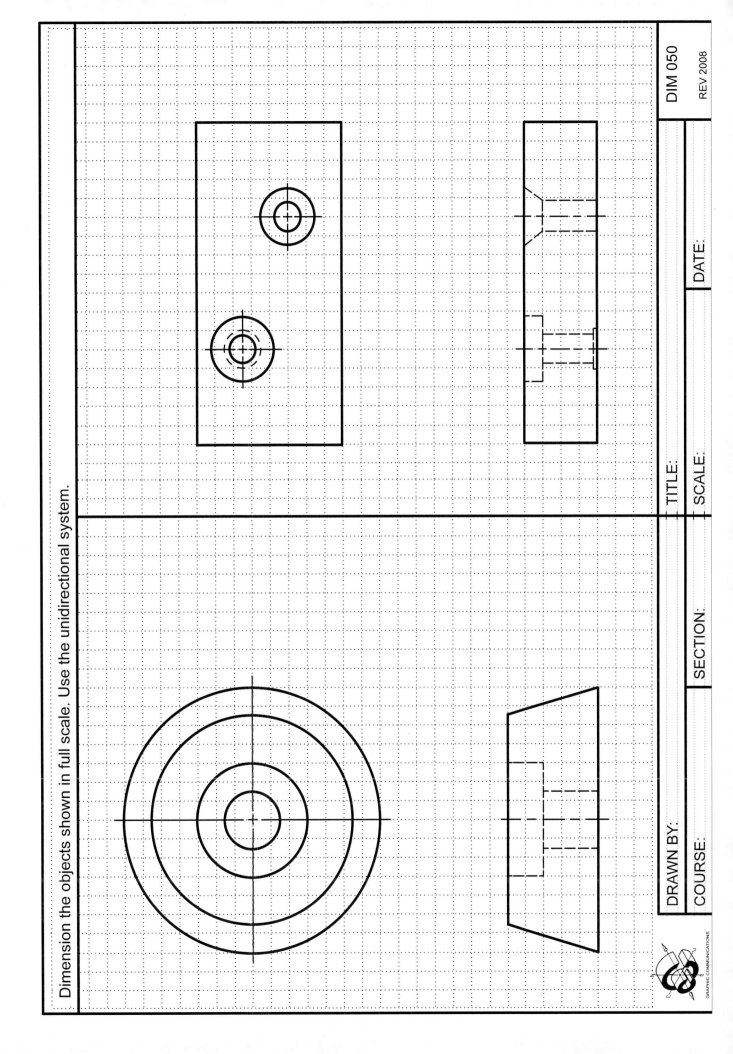

Dimension the objects shown in full scale. Use the unidirectional system.

DRAWN BY:

COURSE:

TITLE:

SECTION:

SCALE:

DATE:

DIM 050

REV 2008

GRAPHIC COMMUNICATIONS

Look carefully at the multiview drawing and make a judgement based on good or poor dimensioning practice. Check your answer on the table below.

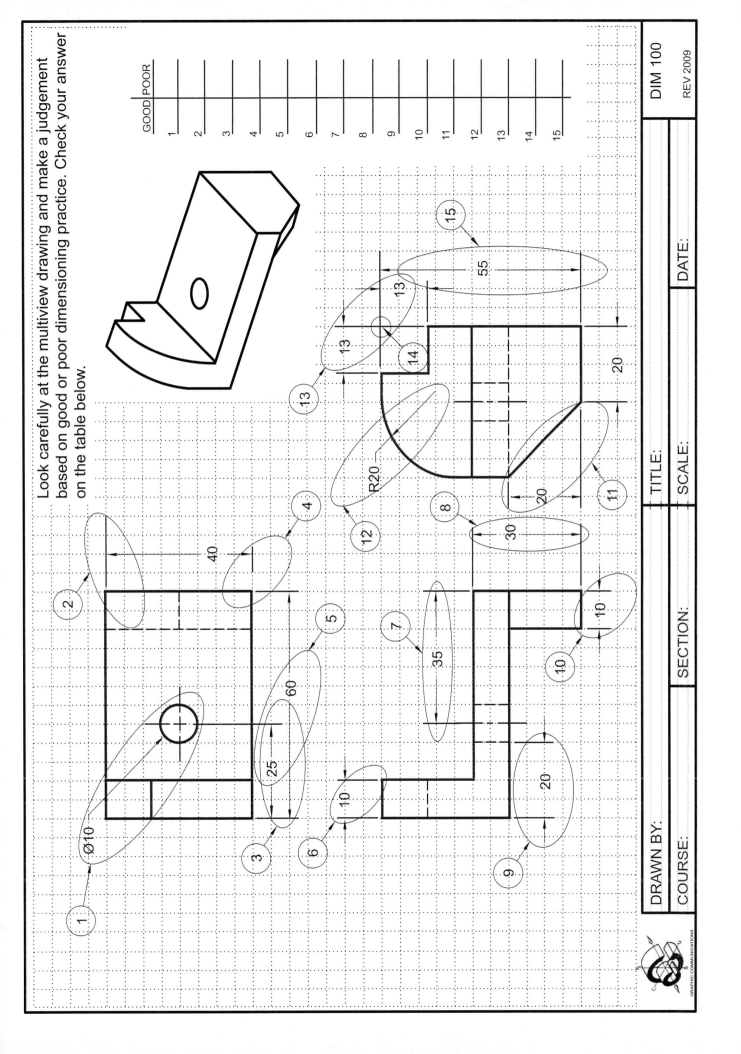

	GOOD	POOR
1		
2		
3		
4		
5		
6		
7		
8		
9		
10		
11		
12		
13		
14		
15		

DIM 100

REV 2009

DRAWN BY:

COURSE:

TITLE:

SCALE:

SECTION:

DATE:

GRAPHIC COMMUNICATIONS

Dimensioning Patterns

1. The dimensioning line closest to the structure: 10 mm away from structure.

2. Next dimensioning lines, where more than one in series: 6mm away from the last.

3. The extension line stops 3mm past the last arrowhead in a grouping.

4. Dimension the holes and arcs where you see the circle or curve.

1.5 mm gap

10 mm

15

6 mm

35

3 mm

5. Circles and Arc more than HALF a CIRCLE

Large

Ø45

Ø15

Small

Diameter symbol: Ø
(placed in front of number)

6. Arcs LESS than HALF a Circle

R20

Large

R10

Small

Radius symbol: R
(placed in front of number)

7. Finish Marks

Types

Finish marks must be placed on the edge view of machined surfaces on rough cast or forged items. It is not necessary to use a finish mark on surfaces where the machine process is indicated.

Finish marks are placed in all views where the surface appears as an edge, even on hidden line surfaces. They must be placed so they are in empty space, not embedded in metal.

A √ shaped finish mark is never turned upside down.

8. Counterbores

Ø16
⌴Ø22
⤓ 10

(Leader must point to center, but no ACTUAL line is drawn.)

Sectional view of a Counterbored Hole

9. Countersinks

Ø6.5
∨Ø12 X 82

Sectional view of a Countersunk Hole

DRAWN BY:		TITLE:		DIM 120a
COURSE:	SECTION:	SCALE:	DATE:	REV 2013

GRAPHIC COMMUNICATIONS

10. Spotfaces

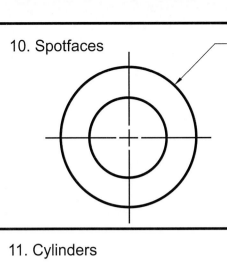

Ø6.5-⌴Ø12

(No depth is usuallly given for a spotface. They are usually only deep enough to create a flat area, on a cast item, so a bolt can lock down and stay tight.)

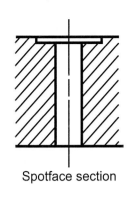

Spotface section

11. Cylinders

The center of a cylinder is locate from the view looking down on it (circular shape), but is sized in profile or from a side view.

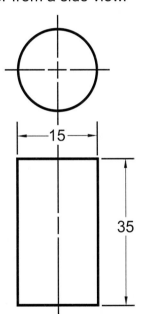

15

35

12. Cylinder with Chamfers

(The length and diameter dimension on the cylinder ignores the chamfer since the chamfer is cut last)

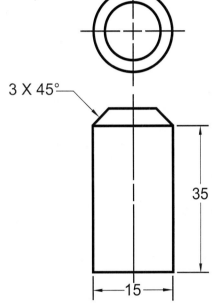

3 X 45°

35

15

13. Fillets and Rounds

Given as a Note:
All fillets and rounds R3 (example)

14. Line Weights

Extension/dimension Lines; Extension and dimension lines drawn with .3/.5 HB lead

15. Guidelines

Guidelines are needed for all numbers

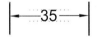

35

16. Multiple holes the same size

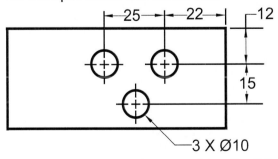

25 22 12

15

3 X Ø10

Holes must be located from two sides. For "blind" holes-holes that do not go completely through-must include a depth.

For drilled holes, depths are only given for the straight portion of the holes.

17. Dimensioning in Degrees

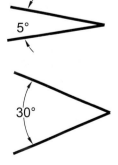

5°

30°

Dimension lines for degrees must be drawn with a compass.

GRAPHIC COMMUNICATIONS

DRAWN BY: TITLE: DIM 120b

COURSE: SECTION: SCALE: DATE: REV 2009

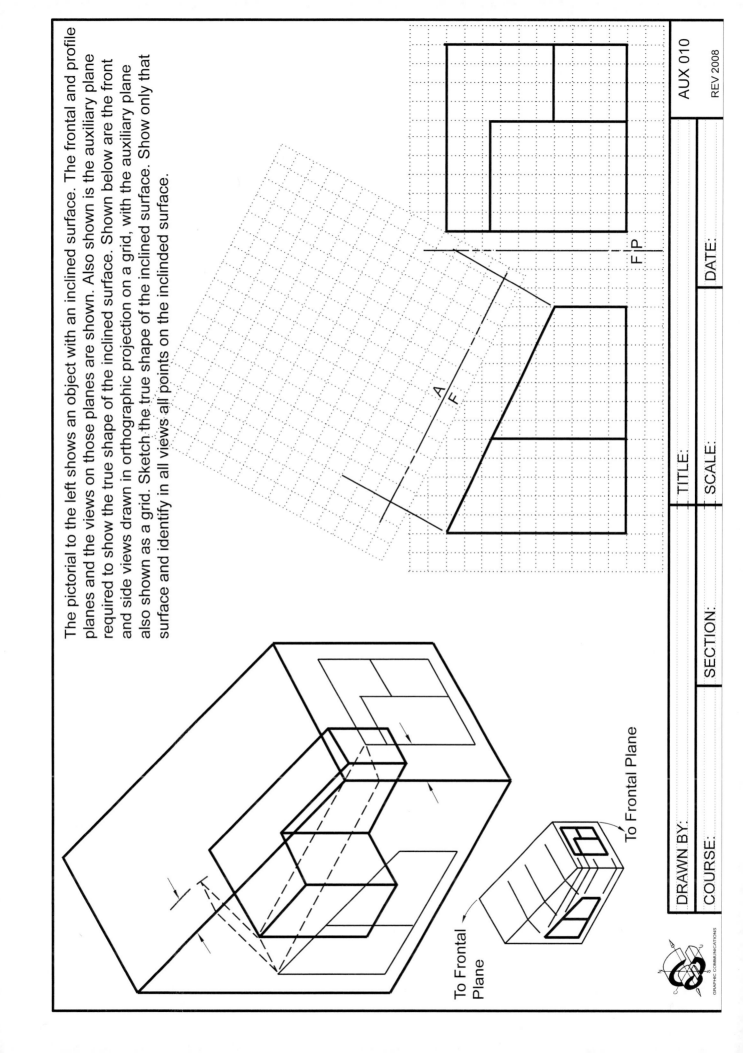

The pictorial to the left shows an object with an inclined surface. The frontal and profile planes and the views on those planes are shown. Also shown is the auxiliary plane required to show the true shape of the inclined surface. Shown below are the front and side views drawn in orthographic projection on a grid, with the auxiliary plane also shown as a grid. Sketch the true shape of the inclined surface. Show only that surface and identify in all views all points on the inclinded surface.

F/P

A

F

To Frontal Plane

To Frontal Plane

DRAWN BY:

COURSE:

TITLE:

SECTION:

DATE:

SCALE:

AUX 010

REV 2008

Sketch the true shape of the inclined surface on the object shown. Use the gridded auxiliary plane provided below. Show only the inclined surface, and identify all points on the inclined surface in all views.

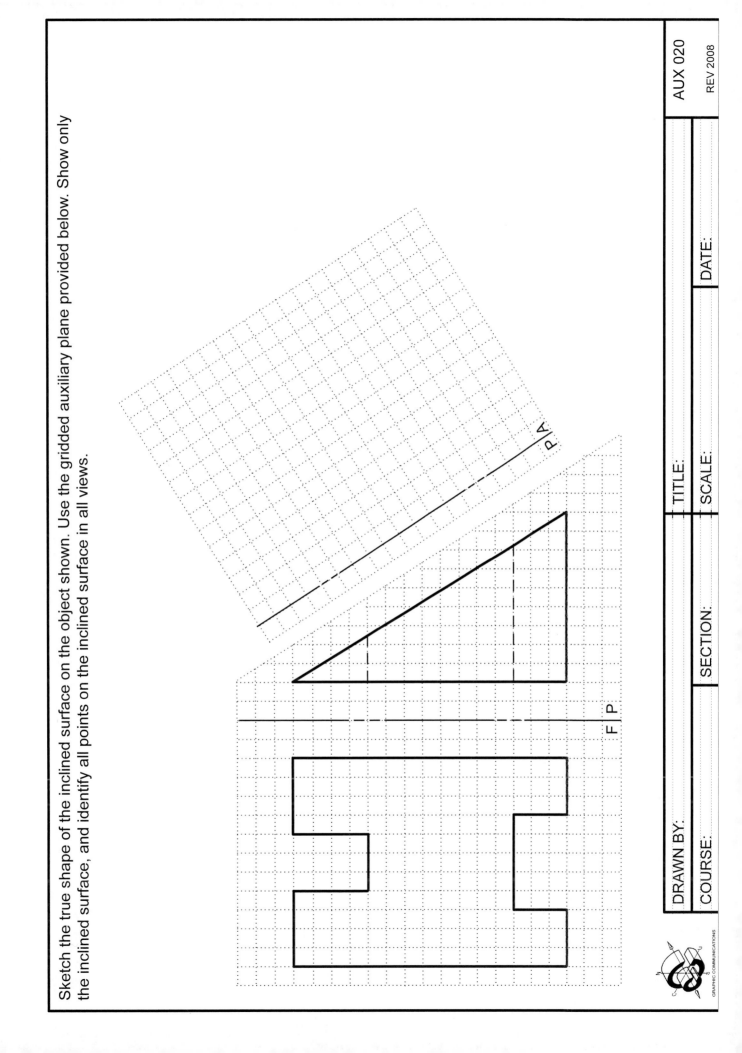

P A

F | P

DRAWN BY:		TITLE:	
COURSE:	SECTION:	SCALE:	DATE:

AUX 020

REV 2008

Sketch the indicated auxiliary view showing the true shape of the inclined surface as indicated by the letter A.

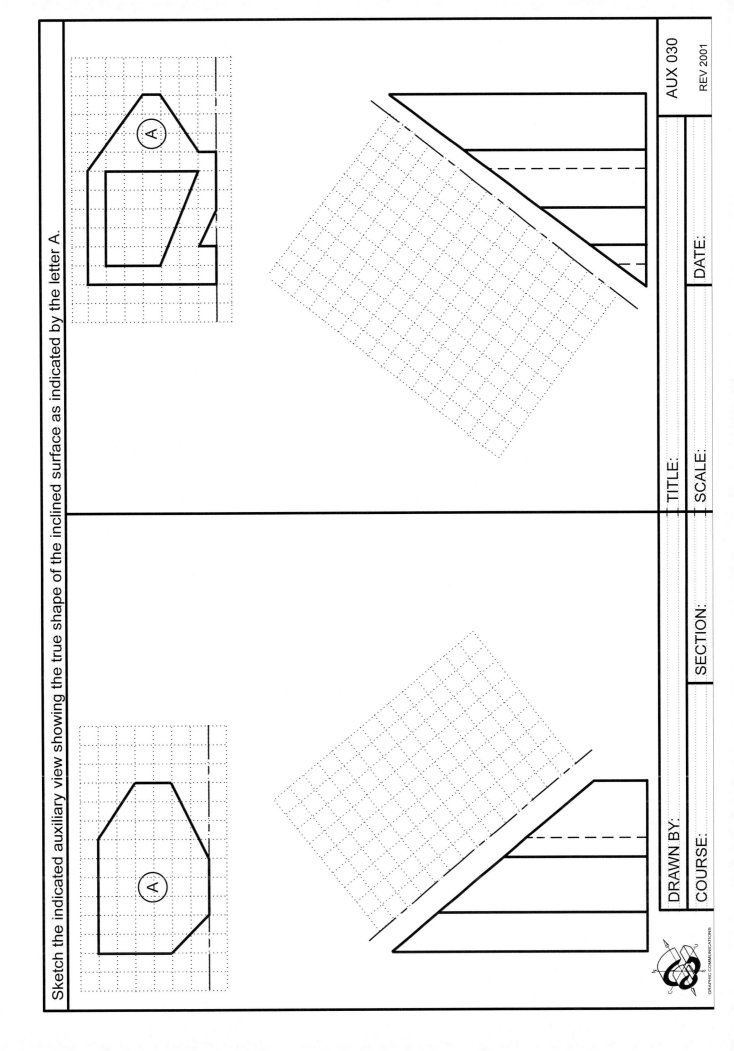

DRAWN BY:		TITLE:	
COURSE:	SECTION:	SCALE:	DATE:

GRAPHIC COMMUNICATIONS

AUX 030

REV 2001

Sketch the true shape of the inclined surface.

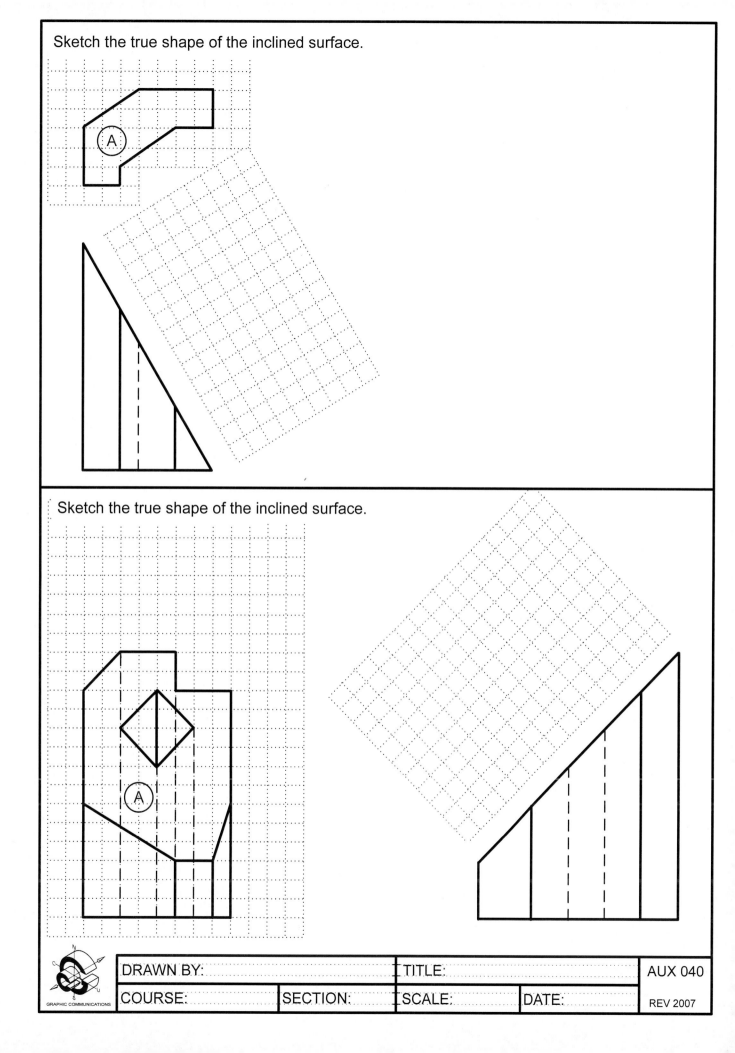

Sketch the true shape of the inclined surface.

GRAPHIC COMMUNICATIONS

DRAWN BY:		TITLE:		AUX 040
COURSE:	SECTION:	SCALE:	DATE:	REV 2007

Sketch a complete auxiliary view showing the true shape of the inclined surface (all edges and surfaces of the object should be shown). Shade in the true shape of the inclined surface. Label the auxiliary view with the points identified in the given views.

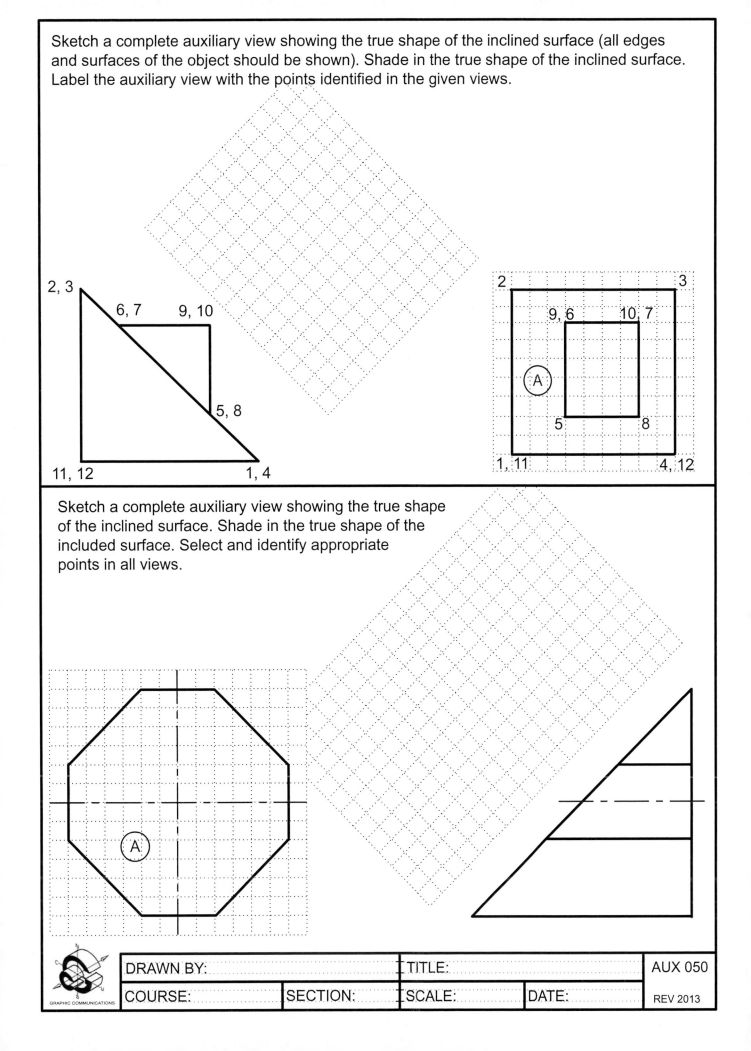

2, 3
6, 7   9, 10

5, 8

11, 12   1, 4

2   3
9, 6   10, 7

A

5   8

1, 11   4, 12

Sketch a complete auxiliary view showing the true shape of the inclined surface. Shade in the true shape of the included surface. Select and identify appropriate points in all views.

A

DRAWN BY: ....

TITLE: ....

GRID
ISO.

COURSE: ....

SECTION: ....

SCALE: ....

DATE: ....

REV 2007

GRAPHIC COMMUNICATIONS

DRAWN BY:

TITLE:

GRID
ISO.

COURSE:

SECTION:

SCALE:

DATE:

REV 2007

GRAPHIC COMMUNICATIONS

DRAWN BY:

TITLE:

GRID
ISO.

COURSE:

SECTION:

SCALE:

DATE:

REV 2007

GRAPHIC COMMUNICATIONS

DRAWN BY:		TITLE:		GRID
				ISO.
COURSE:	SECTION:	SCALE:	DATE:	REV 2007

DRAWN BY:

TITLE:

GRID
ISO.

COURSE:

SECTION:

SCALE:

DATE:

REV 2007

DRAWN BY:

TITLE:

GRID
ISO.

COURSE:

SECTION:

SCALE:

DATE:

REV 2007

GRAPHIC COMMUNICATIONS

DRAWN BY:

TITLE:

GRID
ISO.

COURSE:

SECTION:

SCALE:

DATE:

REV 2007

GRAPHIC COMMUNICATIONS

DRAWN BY: ....

COURSE: ....

SECTION: ....

TITLE: ....

SCALE: ....

DATE: ....

GRID
ISO.

REV 2007

DRAWN BY:

TITLE:

GRID
ISO.

COURSE:

SECTION:

SCALE:

DATE:

REV 2007

GRAPHIC COMMUNICATIONS

DRAWN BY:

TITLE:

GRID
ISO.

COURSE:

SECTION:

SCALE:

DATE:

REV 2007

GRAPHIC COMMUNICATIONS

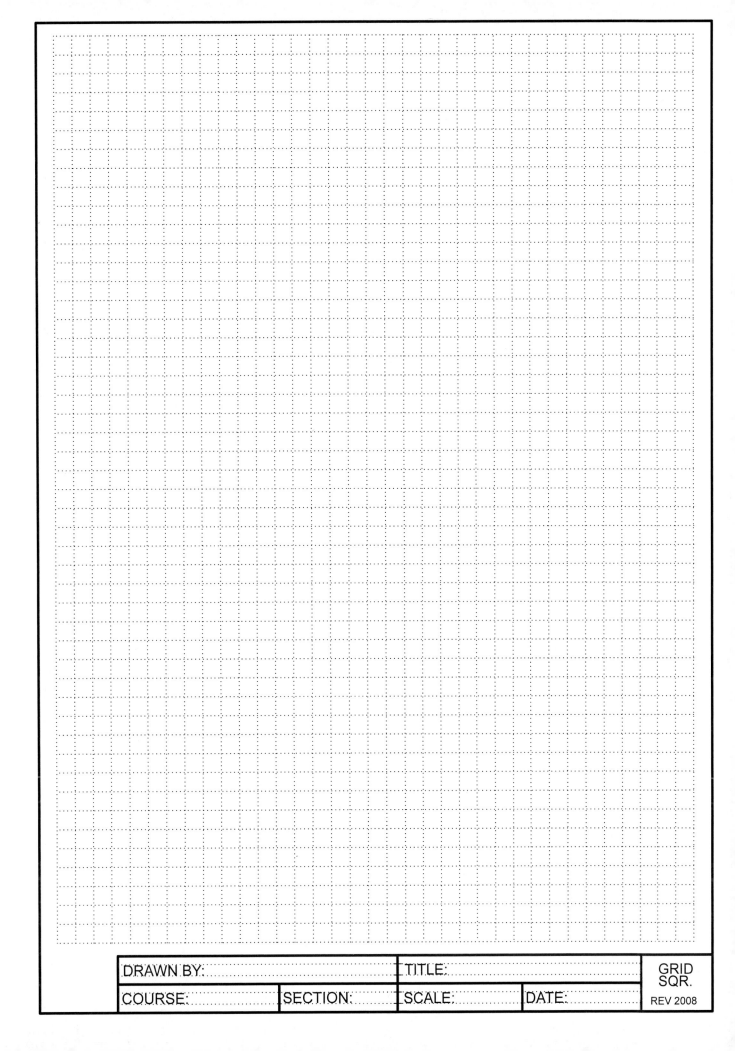

DRAWN BY:

TITLE:

GRID
SQR.

COURSE:

SECTION:

SCALE:

DATE:

REV 2008

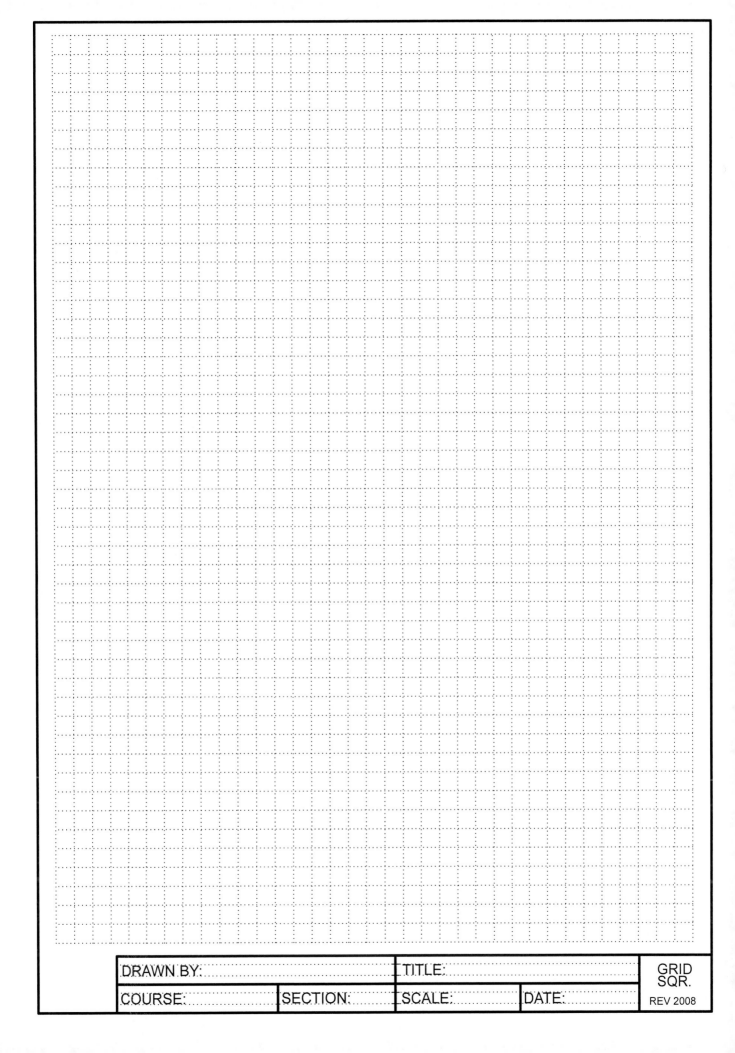

DRAWN BY:

TITLE:

COURSE:

SECTION:

SCALE:

DATE:

GRID
SQR.

REV 2008

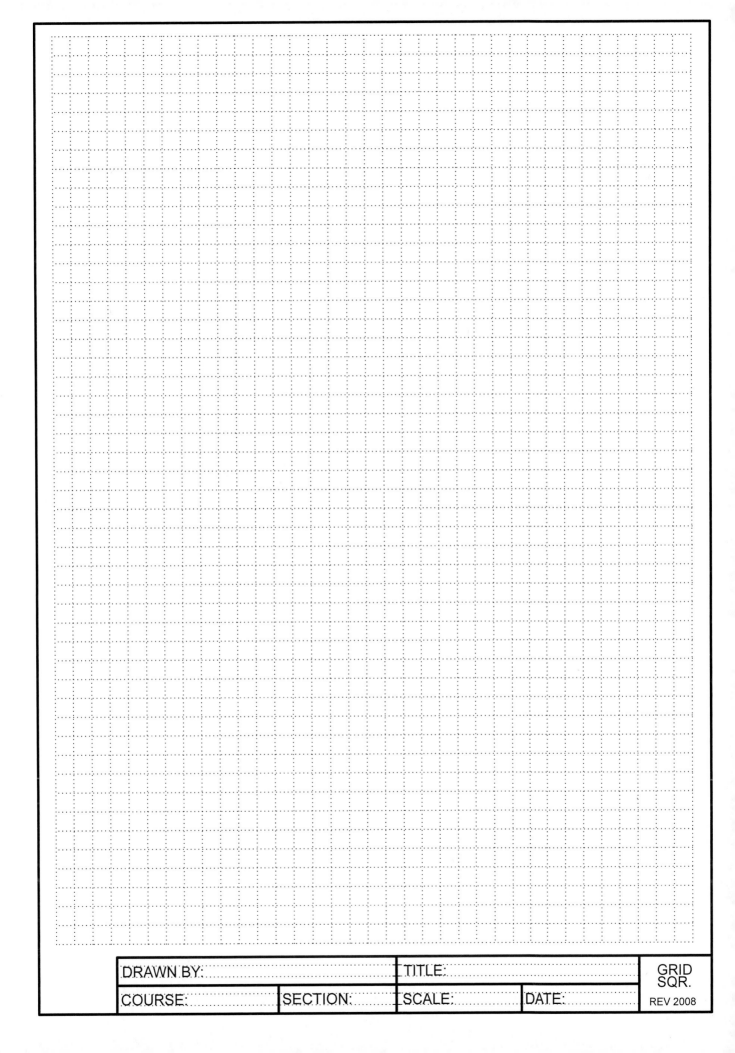

DRAWN BY:

TITLE:

GRID
SQR.

COURSE:

SECTION:

SCALE:

DATE:

REV 2008

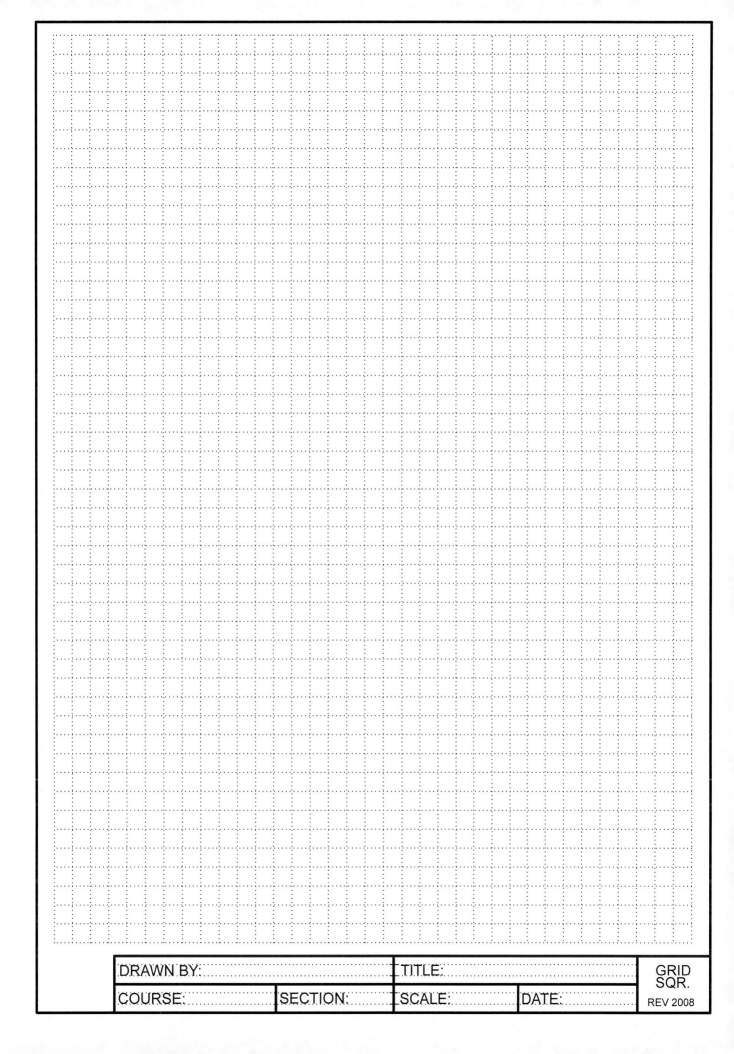

DRAWN BY:

TITLE:

GRID
SQR.

COURSE:

SECTION:

SCALE:

DATE:

REV 2008

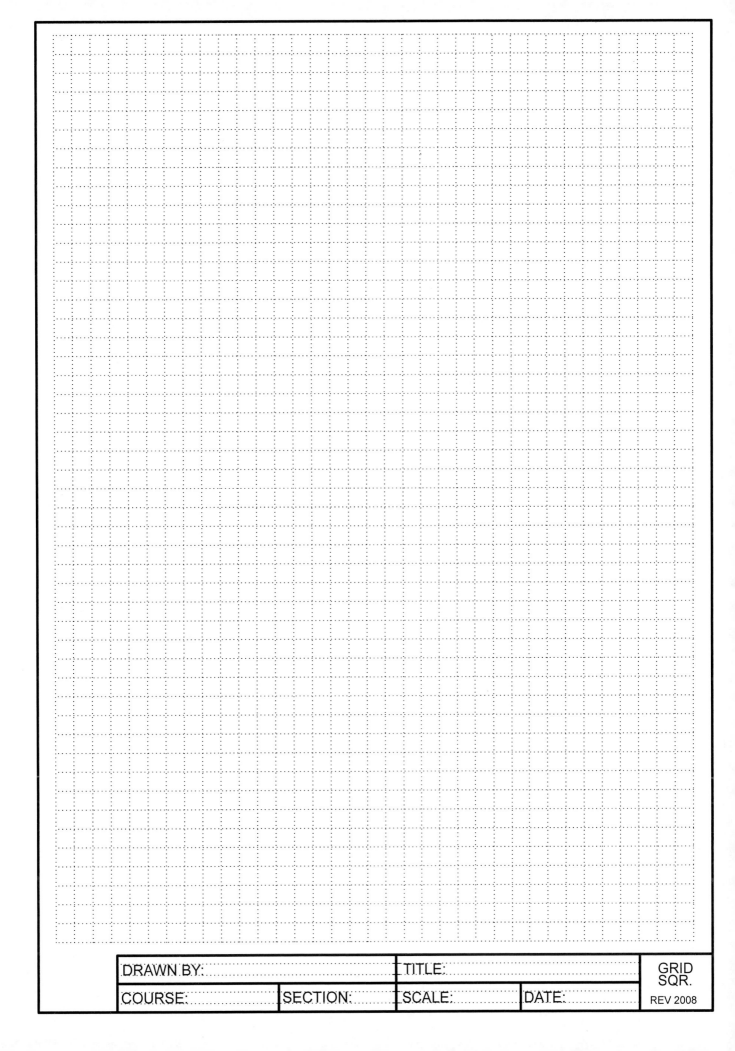

DRAWN BY:

TITLE:

COURSE:

SECTION:

SCALE:

DATE:

GRID
SQR.

REV 2008

DRAWN BY:		TITLE:		GRID
				SQR.
COURSE:	SECTION:	SCALE:	DATE:	REV 2008

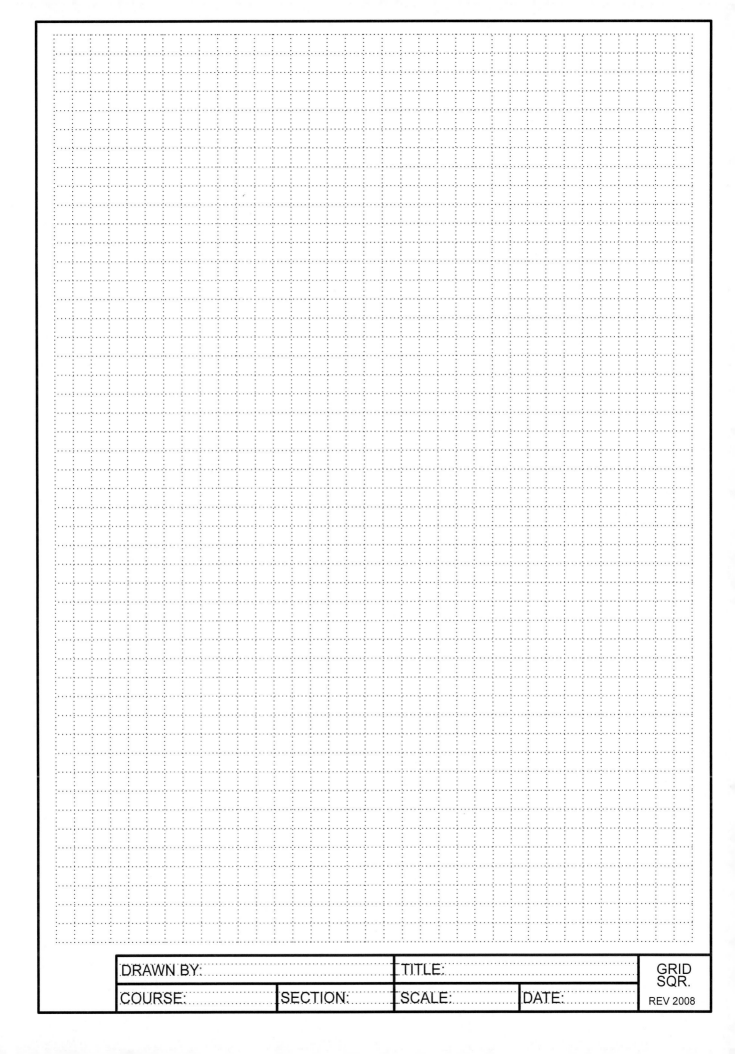

DRAWN BY:

TITLE:

GRID
SQR.

COURSE:

SECTION:

SCALE:

DATE:

REV 2008

TITLE:

DATE:

SCALE:

DRAWN BY:

SECTION:

COURSE:

DRAWN BY:

COURSE:

TITLE:

SECTION:

SCALE:

DATE:

BLANK
HOR.
REV /2008

GRAPHIC COMMUNICATIONS

TITLE:

DATE:

SCALE:

BLANK
HOR.
REV /2008

DRAWN BY:

COURSE:

SECTION:

GRAPHIC COMMUNICATIONS